A GA

It was a combination of luck and talent that led journalist Megan Stevens to Cam Porter's secret hideaway. But Cam was not only the most reclusive star in the film world – he was also an extremely attractive man – who hated all reporters . . .

Another book you will enjoy
by SANDRA MARTON

FROM THIS DAY FORWARD

Caitlin had come to Paris to fight off a merger
between the company she had built up after her
fiance's death, and a French company. She found
support from a totally unexpected source – a source
that was to cost her a lot – emotionally.

A GAME OF DECEIT

BY

SANDRA MARTON

MILLS & BOON LIMITED
15–16 BROOK'S MEWS
LONDON W1A 1DR

First published in Great Britain 1986
by Mills & Boon Limited

© Sandra Marton 1986

Australian copyright 1986
Philippine copyright 1986
This edition 1986

ISBN 0 263 75493 6

Set in Linotron Times 10 on 11½ pt.
01–1086–53,500

Printed and bound in Great Britain by
Collins, Glasgow

CHAPTER ONE

MEGAN STEVENS squirmed on the uncomfortable metal folding chair and stifled a yawn. Whoever had designed this chair was a sadist, she thought. The speaker on the platform at the front of the large, smoke-filled room was still droning on, urging his spellbound audience to improve their lives and their fortunes by purchasing one of the colourfully jacketed books on display at the rear of the room, but Megan was no longer listening. Casually, she reached into the depths of her large handbag and her hand closed around her small, efficient tape-recorder. She'd heard and recorded more than enough, she thought, as she flicked the switch on the tiny machine to 'off'. Two weeks of interviewing disgruntled former members of Inner Success and a day and a half spent pretending to be an entranced new participant in the programme had convinced her that the organisation was, indeed, a fraudulent hoax. It was time to get back to her desk at *Sophisticate* magazine and start hammering out an article for next month's issue.

Megan eased her coat on to her shoulders from the back of her chair and got to her feet. She'd taken a seat near the back of the cavernous room, but her early departure brought frowns to the rapt faces of the people nearest her and caught the immediate attention of the husky young man at the door. He smiled coolly as she reached for the handle and shook his head.

'And where are we going?' he asked brightly. 'Dr Dan told all of us we'd have to stay for the entire afternoon if

5

we want to get the full benefit of his knowledge, didn't he?'

'I've had all the benefit I can take for the moment, thank you,' Megan answered crisply.

The young man frowned. 'I don't think you understand,' he said in a soft, ominous voice. 'We don't leave until we have Dr Dan's approval.'

Out of the corner of her eye, Megan saw a second man moving towards them. He was, if anything, taller and huskier than the first, and there was no smile of any sort on his face at all. She forced a pleasant smile to her lips and batted her eyelashes at the man barring her way.

'Of course we don't,' she whispered. Her voice was husky, she thought fleetingly, not recognisable as her own after a morning spent in what Dr Dan called 'vocal release therapy'. 'All I meant was that I have to . . .' She hesitated and lowered her lashes demurely. 'You see, I was so eager to hear Dr Dan's speech after lunch that I forgot to stop at the ladies' room. I want to get all I can from this session, but if I don't go down the hall for a minute . . .' His suspicious glance flickered to the coat draped over her slender shoulders and she smiled brightly. 'And I'm not looking forward to going into that ladies' room,' she said, forcing a whining tone into her voice. 'It's as cold as a refrigerator. Somebody ought to complain to the manager. You'd think that they'd provide proper heat in a place like this, wouldn't you? Although last winter, in my apartment building . . .'

Relief flooded through her as the man's eyes glazed with boredom. 'Yeah, all right, lady. Just don't take too long. You don't want to miss the next part of Dr Dan's speech.'

'I wouldn't dream of it,' she said brightly, pulling open the door as he stepped aside. 'I'll be back in a jiffy.'

She could feel his suspicious eyes boring through her

back as she walked quickly down the long marble corridor. Deliberately, she paused at the entrance to the ladies' room and turned and smiled at him. He stared at her for a moment longer and then stepped back into the meeting-room and shut the door behind him. Megan took a deep breath, turned the corner, and ran towards the lifts.

'Come on,' she muttered impatiently, pressing the call-bell several times. Warily, she glanced back along the corridor. It was still empty, but for how long? She pushed the bell again, shifting impatiently from foot to foot, until finally the lift arrived and the door slid open.

'Miss . . . wait a minute. Hey, hold it right there . . .'
She caught a glimpse of the two young men from Inner Success racing towards her just as the door closed. There had been rumours about the use of physical force on reluctant new members—in fact, two of the people Megan had interviewed had claimed to have been roughed up when they left the organisation. From the determined looks on the faces of her pursuers, the possibility seemed all too real. The lift was moving steadily downwards. With luck, Megan thought, she would reach the building lobby just ahead of the two who were probably pounding down the stairs this very minute. Quickly, she pulled off her coat, murmuring a sigh of gratitude that it was a reversible one, turned it to its dark brown, twill side and then put it on again. Two levels to go, she thought, glancing up at the floor indicator. She dug into her handbag and dragged out her wool cloche hat. With trembling fingers, she twisted her long, chestnut hair into a topknot, then pulled the hat down over it, tugging on the brim until it all but obscured her face. Just as the lift lurched to a stop, she pulled out a large pair of sunglasses and jammed them on her nose.

Finally, after taking a quick glance into the lobby, she hurried out of the lift and to the front door.

A cold, blustery wind hit her as soon as she stepped into the street. A light snow was falling in the steel and glass canyons of Manhattan, as if to promise that the day would end with the same dreariness with which it had begun. Although it was only mid-afternoon, the lowering sky had already begun to darken. Megan hurried to the corner, trying to lose herself in a crowd of pedestrians fighting their way through the usual tangle of mid-Manhattan traffic as they crossed the street. She felt foolish wearing sunglasses on such a dark day, but she knew no one would notice. New Yorkers had learned to insulate themselves from the constant press of humanity by ignoring anything that seemed unusual, which was not a very comforting thought, for it meant that it was entirely possible that people might simply turn the other way if the two men chasing her caught her. And, even though she could not believe they would really hurt her, she had her tape recorder and her notes to protect . . .

Megan glanced over her shoulder as she reached the opposite side of the street. Yes, she thought as her pulse quickened, there they were, peering up and down the street, looking for her. She yanked the brim of her hat down and pulled her coat collar up. Only another block or two and she'd be at her office. Already, she was imagining her lead paragraph, blocking out the feature she'd write. And this chase through the streets would be part of it, of course, an exciting touch that would make the readers of *Sophisticate* gasp with delighted fear . . .

'There she is! Hey . . .'

There was no need to turn around. She could hear the rapid pound of footsteps behind her, and she began to run. Just ahead on her right was a narrow alley. It seemed to lead towards the next street and, if it did, she might save herself some time . . . The voice behind her called out again, and she knew the men had gained on her. Quickly, her breath rasping in her throat, she swerved towards the alley. There was a barrier of some sort across it, a series of saw horses denying access to pedestrains, but she ignored it, grimly reminding herself that this was no time for paying attention to legal niceties. The pounding footsteps were closer; she could hear her pursuers' ragged breathing in harsh counterpoint to her own, and panic spread its icy touch along her spine. Ahead, a van was angled across the alley, blocking whatever lay beyond from view. What if she'd been wrong? What if there was no access to the next street?

Gasping for breath, legs trembling with exhaustion, Megan darted around the van. Yes, there it was, she thought wildly . . . she could see all the way to the next block, to her office building. And there were people ahead, a small crowd of them. With a shock of pleasure, she realised that most of them were wearing blue uniforms. They were police officers . . .

'Officer . . . hey, officer . . .' Her cry was a breathless call that faded into a horrified gasp as the policeman nearest to her whirled about, his revolver drawn and gleaming in his hand. 'My God,' she cried, 'you don't have to shoot them . . . Wait a minute . . .'

A shot rang out and Megan flung herself to the ground, fear clutching at her heart. What had she stumbled into? Not a street under repair, surely. Was this a robbery? A murder? Did anyone realise she was just an innocent bystander? Was there a story in all this?

'Cut! Dammit, we'll never get this movie filmed. What now?'

Slowly, Megan raised her head. The voice coming from directly above her was petulant and filled with irritation. She looked up into the eyes of a short man chewing on a cigar.

'What's the matter with you, lady?' he growled. 'Don't you know this street is closed? We're trying to film a scene here.'

'I . . . I . . .' She swallowed with difficulty and shook her head. 'A movie? Is that what this is all about?'

The man looked at her with disgust and spat the cigar into the gutter. 'Not any more,' he said at last. 'You've managed to ruin the last shot of the day.'

'Look, I'm sorry. I . . .' Her apology faded into silence as he turned on his heel and stalked off. Awkwardly, Megan gathered up her handbag and began to scramble to her feet.

'Here, let me help you. Are you all right?'

She grasped at the hand that was offered her and stood up, barely glancing at the uniformed man beside her.

'Yes, I'm fine,' she snapped. 'Which are you, a real cop or one of these actors? Because if you are a real one, it seems to me that you could do a better job . . .' She knew that voice, she thought suddenly. She had heard it before. Everyone had. 'You're not a real policeman,' Megan said slowly, raising her eyes to those of the man in blue. 'You . . . you're Cam Porter.'

Still clutching at his hand, she stared into the famous, sexy blue eyes and a faint, embarrassed smile tugged at the corners of her mouth.

'Are you all right?' he repeated. 'I didn't mean to startle you with that shot. It was only a blank, of course, but then you had no way of knowing that.'

Megan nodded her head and smiled again. 'Actually, it came in handy. I was running away . . . well, never mind,' she said, glancing behind her at the empty street. 'It's all over now. I didn't know you were making a picture in New York.'

His eyes narrowed with amusement. 'Is there a reason you should have known? We notified the Mayor's office, the police . . . did we miss your name on the list?'

'I'm with *Sophisticate* magazine,' Megan said quickly, wishing she could whip off the concealing hat and dark glasses and make a more presentable appearance. 'Usually, we know such things . . .'

He dropped her hand and stepped back. 'A reporter?' There was a definite coolness in his eyes as he looked at her. 'Well, that explains everything.'

'Now, just a minute,' Megan began angrily, colour flooding her cheeks. 'What exactly does that mean?'

'It means you have no business here,' he growled. 'This is a closed set.'

'This is a city street . . .' She watched in exasperation as he stalked away from her, and then she hurried after him. 'You owe me a few minutes of your time, don't you think?' Her voice rose as he began to walk more quickly. 'I almost broke my neck because of you, Mr Porter . . .'

He turned towards her just as he reached the door to a large van parked at the end of the block. 'I owe you nothing,' he said evenly. 'If you want a press kit, see my manager.'

Grumbling to herself, Megan squared her shoulders and strode past the short man who had been so unpleasant to her moments before. He'd already acquired another cigar from somewhere, she noticed, and he clamped down on it wetly, glowering at her as she walked past him.

'What's the name of this movie you're making?' she asked, pausing in front of him.

'*Knights of the City*,' he growled, 'if we ever finish shooting it with people like you busting in, playing hell with the schedule.'

Megan smiled cheerfully. '*Knights of the City*, hmm?

I'll be sure to remember it . . . that way, I can be certain I don't have the misfortune to go and see it.' Without waiting for his answer, she turned and hurried across the street towards the towering glass skyscraper that housed the offices of *Sophisticate*.

Moments later, she stepped out of the lift on the fortieth floor of the building and waved hello to the receptionist in the outer office.

'Is Miss Hardwick busy, Gloria?'

The girl smiled and shook her head. 'No, but she's rushing to get out of here early, before the snowstorm hits. I'll ring and tell her you're on your way, Megan.'

Megan nodded and hurried down the hall, towards the rabbit warren of offices in the rear. The door to her editor's office was ajar, and as she pushed it open, she saw Marian Hardwick busily shoving papers into an already over-stuffed briefcase.

'Megan, my dear,' the older woman said as Megan closed the door behind her. 'I'm delighted to see you, of course, but a bit surprised. I thought your meeting at Inner Success was supposed to last until evening. Did it end early because of this awful weather?'

Megan sighed and flung herself into a leather armchair. 'Thank God for something soft to sit in,' she groaned. 'I ache all over after sitting for hour after hour in a damned metal chair with more sharp edges than a block of granite. No, Marian, the meeting wasn't called off. For all I know, those poor souls are still trapped in that airless room, trying to get their three-hundred-dollars' worth of success-training from that charlatan.'

Marian laughed and forced the briefcase closed. 'Well,' she said, sitting down behind her desk, 'I guess that answers the question I was going to ask you. I gather Dr Dan isn't quite the balm to the masses he claims to be.'

'He's an out-and-out fraud, Marian. The guy mixes together a lot of pseudo-psychology and advertising hype, but he doesn't do a thing for the people who sign up for his courses except relieve them of their money. And he has some strong-arm characters hanging around who put the fear of God into those few who begin to smell a rat.' Megan sighed wearily and pulled off her hat, running her fingers through her hair as it tumbled free. 'Believe me, I have more than enough for a great article. I'll have it on your desk by Monday.'

Her editor leaned back in her chair and eyed her narrowly. 'I thought that meeting was held just a few blocks from here, Megan. Isn't it snowing in that part of town, too?'

'Snowing?' Megan repeated slowly. 'Of course it's snowing. It's cold and dreary and dark . . .' Marian's eyebrows lifted inquiringly and Megan began to laugh. 'The sunglasses, you mean.' She took them off and tossed them on to the desk. 'It's a good thing I had them in this bottomless pit of mine,' she said, patting her oversized handbag. 'I had to beat a hasty retreat, and I thought it the better part of valour to change my appearance a little.' Quickly, she told the editor about her flight from the meeting room, leaving out none of the details. 'And then this cop . . . well, I thought he was a cop . . . anyway, he turned around, and then there was a gunshot, and I hit the deck. The director was furious . . .'

Marian shook her head and grinned. 'I don't believe it. You mean to tell me you ran right into the middle of a movie set? Didn't you see the cameras, the sound equipment?'

'I was running for my life, Marian,' Megan said indignantly. 'Well, not quite,' she admitted sheepishly, smiling slightly. 'But I wasn't paying attention to anything but those goons who were behind me. Anyway, who

should come along and help me up but Cameron Porter
. . . *the* Cam Porter, himself. And he was really nice . . .
until he knew who I was.'

'Don't tell me you introduced yourself, Megan,'
Marian said sharply.

Megan glanced at her in surprise. 'No, there wasn't
time. I simply told him I was a reporter, and he turned to
ice.'

'And you had all that stuff on . . . the hat, the glasses
. . . is that right?'

Megan wrinkled her nose and gave an exaggerated
sigh. 'Yes, more's the pity. I mean, if I'd known I was
going to be rescued by the great man himself, I'd have
dressed for the occasion. You know, flowing white
gown, false eyelashes, a diamond tiara in my hair . . .'
She laughed and shook her head. 'Although I suspect it
wouldn't have mattered if I looked like Bo Derek or the
Wicked Witch of the West: he'd still have given me the
cold shoulder, once I said I was a journalist. What's with
that man, anyway?'

Marian shrugged expressively and got up from her
desk. 'Who knows?' she said, walking to a coffee-
machine across the spacious office. 'When he first
started out in Hollywood, he did the usual things young
actors do.' She poured two mugs of steaming coffee and
handed one to Megan. 'You know the stuff I mean—he
showed up at previews, went on whatever television talk
shows he could, gave interviews. Then, when he hit the
top of the box-office charts about ten years ago, he
began to back off a little, but he was still co-operative.'
She settled back into her chair across from Megan and
smiled. 'Of course, he was a real hot item by then
—terrific looks, great acting talent—so the publicity
kept coming, whether he looked for it or not.'

Megan nodded thoughtfully. 'Yeah, I know what you

mean. I see items about him all the time—but they're mostly little bits of gossip. Come to think of it, I don't think I've seen more than half a dozen interviews with him in the past few years, and then he always talks strictly about whatever film it is he's just made.'

'Exactly. The guy has a rule: no questions about his personal life. And if any reporter pushes that, our Mr Porter simply gets up and walks out. He's turned into a real man of mystery.'

Megan sipped at her coffee and then set the mug down on the desk. 'Well, that's not so unusual, is it? After all, Cam Porter isn't the only Hollywood star who keeps a low profile. I mean, just look at somebody like Paul Newman or Robert Redford.'

'Compared to Cam Porter, those two lead lives that are an open book. Would you believe that nobody even knows where the man lives?' Marian waved her hand in the air as Megan started to answer. 'Oh, everybody knows he's got a house on the beach in Malibu, but he's hardly ever there. And sure, he's got a flat here in New York, but he doesn't really live in it. Actually, the guy spends most of his time in Mexico, but the big question is where?'

'Come on, Marian. Where? Where else? Acapulco, Puerto Vallarta, Ixtapa . . .' Megan's eyebrows arched as her editor grinned and shook her head. 'None of those? Well, okay then . . . Mexico City, Guadalajara . . . you're kidding. Cozumel? Cancun?'

The older woman began to chuckle softly. 'The most anybody knows is that he flies his own plane into Durango . . .'

'Durango? Is there really such a place? I thought it only existed in old John Wayne movies.'

'It exists, all right, Megan. It's practically in the middle of nowhere, and nowhere is where our hero vanishes to once he lands his plane. Several reporters followed him that far and then they lost him.'

'They couldn't have tried very hard,' Megan said positively. 'You've got to use a little creativity when you go after somebody who's determined to fade into the woodwork. That's like the time no one could get the goods on that union leader, remember? But I got the story; all it took was a little careful cultivation of his secretary.'

There was a sudden, subtle change of expression on Marian's face. She stared at Megan for a second, and then she swivelled her chair around so that it faced the huge, floor-to-ceiling window behind her.

'Just look at that snow, will you? I'll bet we get six inches before this storm ends. What I wouldn't give to be going somewhere warm right now . . . the way you are, Megan.'

Megan laughed as she put her empty mug on the desk. 'Did I miss something? I thought we were talking about Cameron Porter and his Mexican hideaway . . . Now, just a minute, Marian,' she said quickly as the older woman began to smile wickedly, 'just hold it right there. If you think I'm going to go to . . . to some dusty town in Mexico . . .'

'Durango is a city, my dear,' Marian said mildly. 'A fair-sized one, they tell me.'

'A couple of minutes ago, you said it was in the middle of nowhere. And I have absolutely no intention of riding a burro through some God-forsaken place like that just to get a glimpse of Cameron Porter's home. *Sophisticate* doesn't run teasers like that anyway, and we both know it.'

The editor nodded her head and smiled. 'Precisely. But we are going to run an article about Cam Porter in our next issue. An interview, really, that he gave to us yesterday while you were busy having a terrific time attending an Inner Success workshop.'

Megan groaned and sank back in her chair. 'Don't remind me, please. And I don't understand what you're talking about. If you're going to run an interview with the man, why send me to the ends of the earth just to gawk at his house?'

'Megan, my dear, please give me more credit than that. Our mystery man granted us the interview because he's publicising his new film. As usual, we had to agree to the ground rules in advance. Would you believe he wouldn't even answer a question about whether or not it's true that he's taken up skiing?' Marian shook her head and sighed. 'The point is, every other magazine and newspaper in town will run precisely the same set of dull questions and duller answers.' She leaned forward across the desk and her voice dropped to a husky whisper. 'Meanwhile, the real question . . . the only one worth asking . . . remains unanswered.'

'Where he lives in Mexico?' Megan snorted derisively and rolled her eyes to the ceiling. 'Come on, you've got to be kidding. That's hardly a biggie.'

'You haven't let me finish, my dear,' Marian said patiently. 'You see, about seven years ago, Cam Porter got married. His wife was some sweet young thing from the west coast but almost from the start, the word was that the marriage was in trouble. It was just about then that our Mr Porter began to be less and less accessible to the press, although that didn't stop the stories . . . the more mysterious he became, the more the rumours and gossip flew. Then, suddenly, the wife died. A car crash . . . some perfectly gory mess on a highway in Mexico. That, by the way, was the first time anybody knew that he was living down there. Afterwards, he vanished from the scene for almost a year . . . that's a long time for someone of his stature to go to ground, Megan . . .'

Megan nodded thoughtfully. 'Yes, I seem to recall that. Well, maybe the poor guy was in mourning . . .'

'That's what one wire service said. But the marriage was failing before his wife died, Megan. If that's true, mourning for a year seems a bit excessive, don't you think? I can't believe you haven't heard any of these rumours before . . . where have you been, my dear?'

Megan grinned. 'In the wilds of Arizona until just a couple of years ago, remember? Biology majors don't tend to keep up with this kind of gossip, Marian. And when I switched to journalism, I was too busy making up all the credits I needed to graduate on time to spend my days reading movie magazines.'

Marian smiled archly. 'I still find that fascinating, my dear. To think that you almost devoted your life to test tubes instead of writing. That husband of yours must have been delighted when he discovered your talent.'

'Former husband,' Megan said quickly. 'Please don't leave that word out. Yes, Jeff was pleased. He used to say he was probably the only English professor on campus who stole a student from the science department and converted her to a career in journalism.'

'I still don't understand what went wrong between you two. Student marries professor—that's a fairy-tale ending, Megan. Did your talent begin to frighten him? Was he threatened by it?'

Megan shook her head. 'No, it wasn't like that. He was . . .' She caught herself in mid-sentence and smiled. 'You haven't forgotten how to get a story out of someone, have you? Come on, Marian . . . we weren't talking about me. You were telling me about Cam Porter, remember?'

Marian sighed and shrugged her shoulders. 'Yes, and you're almost as close-mouthed about your personal life

as he is. All right, Megan, we'll get back to Cam Porter.
In fact, I'll give you a crash course in the speculations
about him in the next sixty seconds. Where was I? Oh
yes, his wife's death . . . You see, Megan, it's narrowed
down to two schools of thought. One is that he was with
her when that car crashed, that it was his fault somehow,
and that she didn't die but was hideously disfigured and
he's got her hidden away in some private sanatorium in
Mexico.'

'Come on, Marian . . .'

'The other,' the older woman continued, ignoring the
look of disbelief on Megan's face, 'the other is that she
did die, but that the marriage was so awful that the poor
woman committed suicide, just took the car off a cliff or
into a tree or whatever.'

Megan looked steadily at the woman opposite her.
Finally, she nodded her head. 'I see,' she said in a
toneless voice. 'Either Cameron Porter is playing out a
scene from Jane Eyre—with a crazy wife locked away in
the attic——'

'I didn't say crazy, my dear,' Marian said mildly.
'Disfigured, was the word I used.'

'Okay, disfigured. So he's either got her under lock
and key in a Mexican hideout, or he's got some little
play-pen in Mexico that could drive a woman to suicide.'

'Now, Megan . . .'

Megan shook her head and leaned across the desk.
'Isn't that what you're suggesting?'

The editor sighed and slumped back in her chair.
'What I'm suggesting,' she said patiently, 'is that the
man has some terrible secret locked away. He's one of
the world's most sought-after actors, he's seen everywhere, he gets married. Then, his wife dies—a wife he's
supposedly not even happy with—and suddenly he becomes an ice-man. No more personal interviews, no

more globe-trotting, no making the scene with starlets or anybody else, for that matter. And he runs back to Mexico between films like an animal licking its wounds. What pulls him back there all the time? A terribly ill, deformed wife the world mustn't see? A guilty conscience? You're a reporter for the most popular feature magazine in the world, my dear. Aren't you the least bit curious? Can't you see what a great article you'd have if you answered those questions?'

The office was silent. Even the sounds of traffic from the street far below were muffled, cloaked by the ever-increasing blanket of snow falling from the grey, early evening sky. Megan looked past her editor's questioning face and stared at the tumbling white flakes. A guilty conscience, she mused . . . a guilty conscience. Marian couldn't possibly know how such a thing could distort a life.

Her thoughts raced backward to her former husband, Jeff, and the two years their marriage had lasted. It had taken far less than that for Megan to realise that the strong, assertive man he was in the classroom vanished as soon as his work day ended. His life—and hers, for that matter—was choreographed and arranged by his dominating, interfering mother. As the marriage deteriorated, pulled apart by the stress put on it by three people, Megan had pleaded with Jeff to change, to seek help, but he was blind to the problem. Her last, desperate attempt to wean him away from his mother's control had been a foolish one. She knew that now, but it had seemed to make sense then. If they had a child, she'd thought, if they were a real family . . . From that moment on, the marriage had been all but over. For Megan had learned she might never conceive a child of her own and Jeff—or perhaps it was his mother, for the sentiments they'd voiced had been the same—Jeff said that a woman who couldn't have a child was not really a woman, and he insisted their marriage had failed because of her. Megan's head told her it was all untrue, but still, even now, three years after the divorce, there was a tiny tremor of doubt deep within her, a twinge of uncertainty whenever she thought of Jeff's accusations. Her conscience was clear, but she still wondered if maybe she had been at fault. What if Cam Porter had something to feel guilty about? What if he had a terrible secret buried somewhere near a place called Durango?

'Megan? Are you listening to me?'

'I'm sorry, Marian,' she answered quickly. 'What did you say?'

'I said,' the editor repeated quietly, 'I said that you could get this story, even if no one else has been able to. You got the facts no one could get on that labour leader, you got away in one piece from Dr Dan's goon squad, you did that exposé on welfare fraud last year. Compared to those assignments, this would be a piece of cake.'

'Even if I wanted to . . . he'd recognise me, Marian,' Megan said slowly. 'I spoke to him not two hours ago. He's not a fool.'

'Cam Porter had a sixty-second meeting with a woman wearing dark sunglasses, my dear, a woman with a hat pulled down that hid most of her face. He won't even know your voice, for heaven's sake. What happened to it?'

Megan laughed. 'Awful, isn't it? Don't worry, it's temporary, courtesy of Dr Dan and his group therapy session.' Her laughter faded and she shook her head. 'This kind of reporting isn't my speciality,' she said thoughtfully. 'I don't know much about Hollywood or actors.'

Marian waved her hand as if to brush aside Megan's

words. 'All the better, my dear. You'll come across as a perfect innocent. He'll never suspect you, Megan.' Her eyes narrowed slightly and she smiled. 'By the way,' she said softly, 'I had lunch with Charlie Henson the other day.'

'*Sophisticate*'s publisher?'

The older woman nodded. 'The very same. We talked about the possibility of starting a new column in the spring. "Sophisticated New Yorker", we're going to call it. Charlie thinks you might do well at it, Megan.'

'Marian, that's not fair. You know how badly I want a column of my own. Are you trying to bribe me?'

Marian began to chuckle. '"Incentive" is so much more genteel, don't you agree?'

For a moment, Megan kept a stern look on her face, and then she began to grin. 'Okay, you win. I've got to admit, I'm intrigued. This sounds as if it might turn out to be a pretty good story.' She stood up and walked to the door of the office. 'And it's certainly better than what I was going to suggest for my next assignment.'

'What was that?' Marian called as Megan opened the door.

'How to get across town in a blizzard,' she sighed. 'It looks as if I'm going to be able to write a first-person account by tonight.'

CHAPTER TWO

MEGAN lifted one hand from the steering-wheel of the Ford Escort she had rented and flexed it wearily. Ahead of her, the road seemed to go on forever, a dull grey line climbing ever higher into the rolling, brown-and-green heights of the Sierra Madre Mountains. She glanced at her wristwatch and sighed. Almost three hours had passed since she'd left Durango, and exhaustion was catching up to her.

And with good reason, she thought, stifling a yawn. The flight to Mexico had been long and tiring, the road she was driving was unfamiliar, and her high-school Spanish seemed barely adequate for understanding the Mexican road signs. As if all that were not enough, she hadn't dared take her eyes from Cameron Porter's Land Rover far ahead of her. Her head and shoulders were beginning to ache from the strain.

'He has to stop soon,' she murmured aloud, but the words were more a hope than a statement of fact.

She'd flown into Mexico early that morning, exchanging the snow-bound streets of New York City for the pleasant warmth of a town that looked, at least on the outskirts, like the set from a movie about the Old West. Marian had phoned her in the middle of the night, excitedly telling her that she'd learned that Cam was leaving New York the next day.

'You'll have to leave right away, Megan,' she'd said. 'I've already made your flight arrangements. I'll have a messenger meet you at the airport with a file about Cam Porter. There's not much in it, I'm afraid, but read it on the plane and then, for heaven's sake, get rid of it!'

'Marian, do you know what time it is?' Megan asked groggily, peering at her bedside clock.

'Listen to me, Megan,' Marian pleaded. 'All I've been able to find out is that he's due to reach Durango tomorrow afternoon and that somebody always delivers a Land Rover to him at the airport. You've got to get there before he does. Just remember to be careful . . . Don't let him out of your sight, but don't let him know he's being followed.'

'Don't worry, Marian. He'll never spot me,' she had promised.

And he hadn't, Megan thought with a pleased smile. She'd watched through the telephoto lens of her camera while he alighted from his silver Lear Jet, carefully waiting until he'd stepped into the Land Rover that met the plane before backing her rental car out of the parking lot. At first, she'd worried that the roads in Mexico might be different, but Highway 45 turned out to be as modern and swift-moving as any interstate back home. And Cam was completely unaware of the presence of the Escort following him. Carefully, she'd kept a discreet distance between the two cars, allowing one or two vehicles to get between her and her quarry at times. Megan was certain he'd never even noticed her. Still, once he got to wherever he was going, she knew she would feel a lot safer. The cover story she'd devised would work; the most dangerous part of her plan was picking up his trail at the airport and following him without being seen.

As the hours and the kilometres passed, her sense of security grew. Her great enemy now, she reminded herself, flexing her shoulders, was weariness. But he had to stop soon, even if it was only to have a quick cup of coffee at a cantina in one of the little towns that they occasionally passed. A thrill of excitement ran through her. Perhaps, if he stopped—when he stopped, she assured herself firmly—she might even risk going inside for a cup of coffee as well. After all, he was blissfully ignorant of the fact that she was following him, and nothing about her looked familiar or suspicious. She was wearing no make-up whatsoever, and her long, chestnut hair was drawn back smoothly from her face, hanging down her back in a thick braid. On the seat next to her lay a backpack with a sleeping bag strapped to it. Dressed in an old, faded pair of jeans and a pale blue chamois shirt, she resembled the woman in the cloche hat, dark glasses, and bulky coat that Cam had seen in the alley about as much as Durango resembled Manhattan. And she felt at ease: all the clothing and equipment were things she'd used and loved each time she'd gone home for a visit to her parents' ranch in Arizona, the place where she'd grown up.

Megan reached out and switched on the radio, turning the dial until the gay sound of a Mariachi band filled the car. Everything was going according to plan. This assignment might turn out to be far easier than she'd anticipated, in fact, she told herself, humming along with the music, it looked as though Marian was right. This was going to be a piece of cake.

'That's what it will be,' she warbled, fitting the words to the music, 'a piece of . . . Damn!'

The tyres squealed in protest as she braked and then wrenched the steering-wheel hard to the left. Basking in her own complacency, she'd almost lost the Land Rover as it turned off the highway. Biting her lip, Megan floored the accelerator and the Escort's engine coughed as the little car surged ahead. She'd never have noticed this turn-off, much less believed it was a road, if Cam hadn't swung into it. There was nothing ahead but a single lane of dusty earth climbing straight up into the mountains, except, she noted grimly, straight was precisely the wrong word for it. The narrow road twisted and turned as it wound between rocky mountain walls and tall stands of pine. The Land Rover was out of sight, but the clouds of dust it kicked up were visible signs that it was still ahead of her. Hoping that this was just a short-cut between routes, she kept waiting for the dirt road to connect with another highway, but, as the minutes flew by, she began to admit to herself that such a prospect was unlikely.

Megan took her eyes from the road just long enough to glance down at the fuel gauge. Still half full, she thought with a grateful sigh. Thank goodness for that much. At least the little car wasn't guzzling precious fuel, although she began to wish that she'd had the foresight to rent something with four-wheel drive. Why hadn't she taken a hint from the fact that Cam drove a Land Rover? It was her own fault, she thought angrily. She'd assumed the heavy-duty vehicle was simply a kind of macho affectation, not a necessity. The Escort sounded as if it were labouring on the steep, uphill climb, and her arms ached from steering through the ever-tightening curves of the road.

Megan gasped as she rounded a bend and looked to her left. The edge of the road dropped away beside her, plummeting down into an arroyo that looked to be at least a hundred feet beneath her. Palms sweating, she forced herself to look straight ahead.

'Come on, kid,' she whispered through lips that were suddenly dry, 'you've driven roads like this before. Remember when you used to drive from the ranch back into town? Or when you took that trip into the back country one summer? This isn't any tougher, is it?'

But it was. She had known that country from the time

she was a child, and she'd been driving a Jeep, a rugged vehicle with four-wheel drive that clung tenaciously to the road, exactly like the one somewhere ahead of her. Her eyes darted to the side window again and she shuddered. No guard rail, no dirt shoulder—nothing between her and the canyon below except this awful, narrow excuse for a road . . . and the sun was dipping lower into the slowly darkening sky.

Finally, the land began to rise on her left and Megan sighed with relief as the canyon vanished from view, hidden by a tall stand of pines. It was an improvement, she thought, but only a slight one, for now trees seemed to overhang the road from both sides, crowding in on the straining car and casting dark shadows on the path ahead. Megan raised a trembling hand and wiped her damp brow, glancing at her watch as she did. Lord, they had been climbing the mountain for more than an hour. Where was that damned fool ahead of her going? Was he still up there somewhere? Yes, she could still see the plumes of dust kicked up by his car although there was nowhere else he could be, for there had been no other roads, no place to turn off. She stole a look at the dashboard, worried now that there would be nowhere ahead to get petrol, or to check the ever-increasing rumble coming from the overworked engine. Well, Cam Porter's car wasn't running on air, either. He'd have to stop soon, and that meant that there had to be a better road ahead, or a town, or . . .

The protesting shriek of the Escort's brakes shattered the silence as Megan slammed her foot to the floor. The Land Rover was angled across the narrow road ahead, completely blocking the way, and she had not seen it until she'd rounded a tight curve and spotted its bulk. She fought the wheel as the brakes locked, and the car skidded and came to a shuddering stop, its bumper buried in a soft bank of dirt and tall grass. The engine coughed and died.

Megan sat perfectly still for what seemed to be the longest moment of her life, and then she reached out and shut off the ignition. The rapid thud of her heartbeat drummed in her ears as she raised her eyes from the dashboard and looked out of the window. Cameron Porter was striding down the road towards her. She took a deep breath and wrenched open the car door.

'Are you insane?' she demanded in a voice that sounded more terrified than angry, and she fought to regain control of herself. 'Were you trying to kill me? I could have ended up at the bottom of a gorge, or dangling from a tree, like a Christmas ornament. Why did you block the road that way?'

'So I could stop you from following me,' he said calmly, 'and I did just that, didn't I?' He stopped a couple of feet from where she stood and looked her over carefully. 'Are you all right?'

'Am I all right?' Megan repeated incredulously. 'Do you really care? For God's sake, you almost killed me.'

He smiled slightly and shook his head. 'That's something of an overstatement, I think. You weren't going that fast and besides, I know every inch of this road and I picked my spot very carefully. There's nothing but soft dirt and grass on either side for the next few hundred yards. Anyway, I've been watching you in my rear view mirror for the last few hours; you drive well enough so I didn't have any real worry about you getting hurt.'

Megan wiped her hands on the seat of her jeans and nodded her head. 'Well, that's very kind of you, I'm sure,' she said in a voice dripping with sarcasm. 'It's really terrific to know that you picked the spot with such concern for my welfare. I'm deeply touched. And what do you mean, you've been watching me? I didn't even know there was another car on this road.'

Cam shook his head in a quick gesture of irritation. 'Come on, you can do better than that. You've been tailing me for quite a while. I thought it was time I found out who you were.'

She took a deep breath and forced her eyes to meet his without flinching.

'Is that why you ran me off the road? You mean, you're not only a maniac who likes to watch accidents happen, you're also a . . . a paranoid lunatic who thinks every person on the road is following him?' She shook her head and turned towards her car. 'Goodbye, Mr Whoever You Are. I don't think I want to stand around talking to you for a minute longer than I have to. Don't think it hasn't been fun . . .'

He reached out and grabbed her arm. 'I asked you a question,' he said quietly. 'Who are you? And what do you want with me?'

'Look here . . .'

'No, you look here,' he said in an ominous voice, his fingers biting through her chamois shirt. 'You aren't going anywhere until I get some answers. I want to know what you're up to, and there isn't much point in looking around for help. There probably won't be another car along this road until tomorrow. Not too many people come this way at the best of times, and sunset certainly isn't one of them.'

Megan swallowed the metallic taste of fear in her mouth and wrenched free of his grasp.

'This is a public road,' she said, surprised at how calm and assured she managed to sound, 'and I have every right to be on it. It's none of your business, but if it makes you feel any better, I'll tell you why I'm here. I'm a graduate student in wildlife biology,' she said quickly, plunging into the cover story she had so carefully prepared. 'I'm heading up into the Sierra Madres to do some field studies. So, unless you're interested in bobcats, puma, or wolves, you have nothing to fear from me.'

Cam smiled coldly. 'That's an interesting choice of words. Why do you say that? What would I have to fear from you?'

She groaned inwardly at the slip she'd made. 'I simply meant that you seem afraid I'm following you. Well, I'm not. Really. I just took the first road that led up into the area my professor had suggested. I didn't realise it would be so deserted.' She forced a pleasant smile to her face and gazed up at him with perfect innocence. 'Do you live around here?'

His eyes flickered past her to the Escort. 'You'd better turn around and head down the mountain,' he said gruffly, ignoring her question. 'There's only about half an hour of daylight left, and you're going to find it rough going in the dark.' Quickly, he turned and started up the road towards his Land Rover. 'Your professor should have steered you to a safer area. And you can add grizzlies to that list of animals you plan on observing,' he called back over his shoulder. 'There's quite a healthy population of those, too.'

She stared at him in disbelief. He wouldn't just leave her here, she thought wildly. He couldn't . . .

'Wait a minute,' she called, taking a hesitant step after him. 'Aren't you going to help me get my car started? You can't just drive off . . .' Suddenly, the full impact of what he'd said struck her. 'Grizzlies?' she repeated. 'Did you say there were grizzlies in these mountains?'

The door of the Land Rover slammed shut and the engine roared into life.

'Yeah, but I wouldn't worry too much about the

bears,' he yelled as he backed his car up into the road. 'After dark, it's mostly the big cats that prowl these hills. Just don't get out of your car until you reach the highway, and you should be fine.'

'Hey, wait . . .' Megan's shouted plea for help hung unanswered in the sudden silence as the Land Rover rounded a bend in the road and vanished from sight. She coughed as a cloud of dust drifted over her, and then turned glumly towards her car.

'You certainly are a true gentleman, Cam Porter,' she muttered as she yanked open the door and got in. 'But you can't shake me off that easily.' If she hurried, she could be on his trail in just a few minutes. He'd have to turn off somewhere, and when he did, she'd be right behind him. Quickly, she turned the ignition key. The engine whined sadly, and then stopped with an ominous thump. 'Damn! she moaned, hissing through her teeth. Holding her breath, she turned the key again, this time, there was no response at all from the engine.

Angrily, she wrenched open the door and stepped out into the road. It was completely deserted and silent, and the sun had dropped low enough on the horizon so that there was an uncomfortable chill in the air. She stalked to the front of the car and opened the bonnet. There were wires and belts everywhere, but peering in at them told her little except that they all seemed to be properly attached. Slamming the bonnet closed, Megan bent and looked under the car. With an anguished groan, she reached out and touched the dark, wet patch spreading underneath. It was sticky and oily to the touch.

'Double damn!' she shouted, straightening up and kicking the nearest tyre in frustration. 'I hate you, Cameron Porter,' she yelled into the surrounding silence. And yet, she realised with sudden distress, it wasn't really as quiet as she'd first imagined. There was a rustling sound coming from the tall grass growing on the slope to her right, and the shrill cry of an animal drifted down to her from somewhere ahead.

Suppressing a shudder, trying not to dwell on how rapidly the sun seemed to be setting, Megan got back into the car and locked the door after her. There was nothing to be afraid of, she told herself sternly. She had grown up in country almost as wild as this, hadn't she? And she knew a lot about wild animals; after all, you couldn't grow up surrounded by cattle and horses without learning something about the predators that preyed on them. Still, she thought nervously, fighting against the urge to look back over her shoulder, there weren't any wolves in Arizona. And grizzlies were a species she knew little about, except that they were big, mean, unpredictable and . . .

'Stop it,' she whispered aloud. 'You're behaving like a child.' She took a deep breath and took stock of her situation. She had a sleeping bag, so even if the night grew cold, she'd be comfortable. And there were a couple of granola bars in her backpack. The biggest problem she faced was losing Cam's trail, but even that wasn't insurmountable. As rugged as he'd looked, dressed in faded denims and a chambray shirt, with a sheepskin jacket slung around his shoulders, he couldn't possibly drive much further. He had to be tired; he'd flown his own plane into Durango and then driven for as many hours as she had. Wherever he was going, it couldn't be too far away. In the morning, at first daylight . . .

An animal streaked across the dirt road just a few feet from the car. It moved too quickly for Megan to identify, but whatever it was, it was big. Hastily, she checked the locks on the other doors and rolled up her window. It was almost dark, and it occurred to her that soon she would have to leave the safety of the car and check the boot to see if there were any flares in it. If there were none, staying in the car might be as dangerous as spending the night out in the open. Cam had said no one would use this road after dark, but what if he was wrong? Someone driving up the mountain would never see her car until it was too late.

Fighting against the urge to stay safely inside, Megan opened the door warily. She thought of getting her flashlight out of the backpack on the seat beside her, but there was still enough faint light to see by, and she had no desire to begin wearing out the battery so early in the long hours of darkness that were to come. Again, she thought of Cam Porter and cursed the cruel arrogance that had allowed him to create this situation and then abandon her to fate without hesitation. Tears of anger and frustration welled in her eyes and she blinked them back, determined not to give in to the fear and self-pity that were slowly eroding her ability to concentrate.

She stepped out of the car and walked around it, her hand trailing along its length, taking comfort from the solid feel of it beneath her fingers. The lid of the boot swung open and she closed her eyes in despair after she peered inside. There were no flares.

There was a quick, scurrying sound in the grass across the road and an animal squealed once and was silent. Megan shivered and wrapped her arms around herself. There was no longer any doubt as to where she'd spend the night, she admitted, hurrying back towards the front of the car. Flares or no flares, she'd get into the car and lock the doors.

Suddenly, her head sprang up and she held her breath. Was it possible? Was that a car she heard? Wild excitement flooded through her as approaching headlights pierced the gloomy shadows that hung across the road ahead. She danced out into the middle of the road, waving her arms and shouting, and then, slowly, her arms fell to her sides and the smile faded from her face.

It was Cam's Land Rover. As it drew to a stop next to her, she stared at it in disbelief, caught between a sweeping sense of relief and maddening anger.

'Well,' he said gruffly, reaching across and opening the door, 'are you going to stand there gaping at me all night, or are you going to get in?'

'I . . . I need some things from my car . . .'

'Then get them,' he growled, 'and be quick about it.'

Hurriedly, Megan collected her backpack and jacket from the disabled car and climbed into the Land Rover. She glanced over at Cam as he backed up and turned the car around. In the faint light from the dashboard, it was impossible to read the expression on his face, but Megan had the feeling that it was not a pleasant one. She bit down on her lip to keep from crowing. Her misfortune had suddenly turned into the greatest kind of good luck. Here she was, in the middle of nowhere, alone with the man she had travelled thousands of miles to write about. And he was responsible for it, not she!

Twilight had given way to the blackness of night. Cam said nothing as the Rover moved steadily through the darkness, concentrating instead on driving along the tortuously winding road with a speed that seemed suicidal to Megan. Perched on the edge of the seat, trying to peer ahead into the night, she could only glimpse some of the wild terrain they sped through. She sensed that he was looking at her, and glanced in his direction.

'Put your seatbelt on,' he ordered brusquely. 'I know every turn and bump in this road, but anything is possible in the dark.'

Obediently, she buckled herself into the shoulder harness and sat back. She waited for him to say something else, but he remained silent. Finally, she cleared her throat hesitantly.

'Thanks for coming back for me,' she said, trying to draw him into polite conversation.

'I didn't have much choice, did I? I told you that there were predators that prowl these hills at night, and I had the feeling you might not be able to get your car turned around . . .'

Megan's determination to be pleasant was swept aside as she heard the irritation in his voice.

'It wasn't quite that simple,' she snapped. 'The damned car wouldn't start. There was oil gushing out of it—something must have ruptured when you ran me off the road.'

He looked over at her and she saw him grin in the faint light. 'You ran yourself off the road,' he said calmly. 'And even if your car had started, you'd never have been able to get down to the highway in the dark without running into trouble.'

'You were the only trouble I ran into,' she said coldly. 'Believe me, if you hadn't interfered, I'd have managed this road with no difficulty.'

'I doubt that,' he said so positively that she flushed with anger. 'At any rate, there's not much use arguing about it now. You'll have to arrange to have the car towed.'

'Is that where we're going? To a garage?'

Cam laughed and shook his head. 'You really don't have any idea of where in the hell we are, do you? The nearest garage is down this mountain and about fifty miles back towards Durango. There's nothing ahead of us but a couple of scattered villages. No, a garage will have to wait for tomorrow.'

Megan reached out and held on to the dashboard as the Rover bounced over a bump in the road.

'Then where are we going?'

'To a place where you can stay the night and arrange for a tow and a ride back to Durango bright and early in the morning.'

Again, she felt his eyes upon her, and she forced herself to meet his gaze.

'You don't have to look at me that way,' she said defensively. 'It isn't my fault all this happened. You're the one who blocked the road.' He said nothing, and she sighed. 'Are we going to an inn in one of those villages you mentioned?' she asked finally. 'How can you be sure they'll have room for me?'

'You can't know as little about these mountains as it seems,' he said angrily. 'You said you were out here to do a graduate field study—then why don't you have more knowledge of the area?' A suspicious note crept into his voice. 'Maybe I shouldn't have asked who you were, but if you know who I am?'

'Of course I know who you are,' Megan answered quickly, a warning chill running through her. 'You're some sort of crazy man who thinks he owns all the roads in Mexico, and I resent your implying that I'm un-prepared,' she added angrily, hoping the lie would sound convincing. 'Naturally, I know something about this area. I just didn't expect to have a car wreck before setting up camp, that's all.'

There was a sudden break in the trees to the left side of the road, and Cam swung the Land Rover on to an even narrower track than the one on which they'd been driving. Suddenly, a small animal appeared ahead, illu-minated in the bright glare of the headlights, and Cam jammed on the brakes.

'It's a bobcat,' Megan whispered with honest delight.

'It's so rare to see them . . . I once camped out for days, just hoping for a glimpse of one.'

The green fire of the wildcat's eyes fixed on them with a mixture of fear and defiance for a few seconds, and then the animal raced back into the brush. Cam moved the car forward slowly.

'Well, you've come to the right place, if seeing cats makes you happy,' he said. 'Sometimes, I think that's all we have up here. Cats preying on foals, on calves . . .' He broke off in mid-sentence, as if he'd said more than he planned. 'We've arrived,' he said finally. 'Make sure you take everything you need from the car.'

Megan peered through the window. If they had reached some sort of destination, she had no idea what it was. She could see only blackness ahead. Then, suddenly, the car swung into a clearing, its headlights picking out fences of some sort on either side. There was a low-slung, sprawling house set at the end of the clearing. It seemed to sit huddled at the base of a mountain peak that all but blocked out the stars, but the light was so poor that her impressions were fragmented. Cam leaped from the car and started towards the house, and she snatched up her things and scrambled after him, unwilling to be left behind in the darkness.

She hurried up the gravel pathway after his retreating figure, almost unable to believe what was happening. There were no inns up here, he'd said. Then this place, this isolated house, must belong to him. And she, more through his actions than through her own planning, was about to enter it. She fought back the wild desire to laugh aloud in triumph, and caught up to him just as the massive front door was thrown open.

A dark-haired, heavy set woman stood in the lighted doorway, smiling and wiping her hands on her apron.

'*Buenas noches, Señor*. It is good you have arrived.

We were growing concerned . . .' The woman stared past Cam and her eyes widened with surprise as she caught sight of Megan. '*Señor?* You have brought a guest?'

'Good evening, Maria,' Cam said brusquely. 'This young woman had a car accident, and she needs a place to stay for the night. Will you please show her to the guest-room?' He turned to Megan and motioned towards her. 'Maria will show you where you can wash and put your things.'

Megan smiled as she stepped into the foyer. 'Thank you,' she began. 'I'm really very grateful . . .'

'Don't be,' he growled. 'I'm only doing what had to be done. Maria will bring you a tray; I suggest you eat and then get some rest. You're going to make an early start. Now, if you'll excuse me, I'll go and make arrangements for someone to pick you up and tow your car down the mountain tomorrow.'

The smile faded from Megan's face as he stalked away from her. It was too much to expect that he would invite her to join him for dinner. After all, she wasn't really a welcome guest in this house. He had brought her here out of a sense of duty, and that in itself said something about him. Perhaps Marian was right; perhaps there was some secret, something that wore on his conscience and kept him in this isolated wilderness.

That she had made this much progress on the very first day in her quest seemed a miracle, she thought, following the housekeeper through the open-beamed foyer towards a hall that led to a far wing of the house, progress that couldn't be tarnished by worrying about what would happen tomorrow. Somehow, Megan promised herself, she would find a way to prolong her stay. Cam was not pleased to have her here—that much was certain—but he'd accepted her cover story. And here she was, successfully tucked away inside this hidden lair in the mountains.

Already, she knew more about him than any of the reporters who'd come to Mexico before her. And this was just the beginning.

CHAPTER THREE

MEGAN awoke to the sound of a gentle tapping at her door. She stretched slowly, shivering slightly as her bare arms came free of the brightly patterned Mexican blanket and felt the chill of the early morning air. She had gone to bed early, tired from the day's events and had slept heavily.

'Yes?' she mumbled sleepily. 'What is it?'

The door opened a bit and Maria stuck her head into the room. 'Breakfast is ready, *Señorita*. You would like a tray brought to you? As last night?'

Megan nodded and yawned. 'Oh, yes, thank you, Maria. I'm dying for some coffee.' Suddenly, she frowned and sat up in the bed, clutching the blanket to her. 'Wait,' she called, just before the housekeeper closed the door. 'Is *Señor* . . . is the gentleman who brought me here having breakfast in his room?'

Maria shook her head and smiled. 'He is already on the patio, *Señorita*. That is where he always breakfasts.'

'That's fine, then,' Megan said quickly. 'Never mind the tray; I'll be out in just a couple of minutes.'

The housekeeper's smile broadened. '*Sí, Señorita*. You will find the patio down the hall and *a la derecha* . . . to the right.'

'*Sí, Maria. Gracias,*' Megan answered, returning the woman's smile.

As soon as the door had closed, Megan sprang from the bed and hurried into her clothing. Pulling the clip from her braided hair, she brushed it until it fell in a glistening cascade around her face, then glanced into the

40

mirror above the dresser, winking at her own reflection. There was no harm in looking a little softer, a little prettier this morning, she thought. If she was going to find a way to persuade Cam Porter to put up with his uninvited and unwanted guest a bit longer, it couldn't hurt to use every available resource.

She tucked her hairbrush into her backpack and hesitated as her fingers touched the camera stuffed deep inside. Soft, early morning sunlight filled the handsome guest-room, illuminating it so that every detail stood out in sharp relief. What a great picture it would make, she thought, admiring the knotty pine walls, the heavy oak furniture, and the flashes of colour provided by the hand-woven Mexican blankets draped across the bed and chairs. Quickly, she picked up the camera, adjusted the settings, and snapped off several shots from different angles. The one thing lacking in the photos would be any signs of Cam Porter's personal life, but she could solve that problem later, when she found a way to tour the rest of the house. She patted the camera happily and tucked it back into the depths of her pack.

Moving swiftly, trying to make up the precious time she'd wasted, Megan followed Maria's directions to the patio, fighting against the temptation to glance into any of the rooms she passed as she hurried down the corridor. She peered out of the sliding glass doors and drew a sigh of relief. Yes, Cam was still there, leaning casually against a low wall of dark stone, sipping a cup of coffee and looking towards the snow-topped mountain peaks that broke the horizon into jagged shards of blue. Megan paused, aware of how contented and peaceful he seemed, how handsomely he fitted into this rugged, beautiful setting, and then she took a deep breath and slid the door open.

'Good morning,' she said brightly, crossing the

terracotta tiled patio towards him. 'It's a lovely day, isn't it?'

He turned to her with a look of surprise on his face. 'I didn't expect to see you just yet. I told Maria . . .'

'She offered me breakfast in my room, but I thought I'd make things easier for her by joining you out here,' Megan said quickly, hoping she could head off any protest he might make. 'That coffee smells delicious,' she added, smiling at him. 'Do you mind if I . . . ?'

He scowled and shook his head. 'Have some, by all means,' he said, gesturing towards a round pine table. 'I suppose you'd like something to eat, too.'

Megan forced herself to continue smiling as she poured herself a cup of coffee, although his statement sounded more like an accusation than an offer of hospitality.

'I certainly would,' she said brightly. 'It must be the mountain air. I'm absolutely starved!'

Cam nodded and put his empty cup on the table. 'Well, I'm certain Maria will see to it you're well fed. If you'll excuse me . . .'

Megan's eyes darted from the table, empty except for the coffee service, to Cam's face.

'I didn't realise you'd already eaten. Maria should have told me . . .'

'She offered to bring a tray to your room,' he said bluntly. 'You should have accepted it. I've already had my coffee, and I prefer to have it in privacy.'

Her face reddened as he spoke. 'I'm sorry,' she answered slowly. 'If you like, I'll . . .'

'*Buenos días,*' Maria called cheerfully. 'If you would be so kind as to open the door, *por favor* . . . *Gracias, Señor.* I think the cool mountain air has given the *Señorita* an appetite, *sí*?'

Cam's scowl had deepened as he watched Maria set a

heavily laden tray down on the table.

'What is all this?' he asked curtly. 'Maria, you know I never have such a large breakfast.'

The woman smiled disarmingly and shrugged her shoulders. 'But this is such a special morning, *Señor*. You have a guest . . . I thought it would be pleasant for you both.' Her smile faded, almost by design, Megan thought, and she bowed her head slightly. 'But if I have displeased you, *Señor* . . .'

To Megan's surprise, Cam shook his head and sighed. 'No, Maria, of course not. It was a fine idea. Actually, I can hardly wait to get at those eggs.'

Maria grinned happily and wiped her hands on her apron. '*Bueno*. If you need anything more, just call.'

There was a moment of uncomfortable silence after the housekeeper had left, and then Cam cleared his throat.

'Well,' he said gruffly, 'we can't very well disappoint her after she went to all this trouble.' He turned away from Megan's bemused stare and lifted the cover from a large, silver platter. 'I hope you like this kind of food . . . she's certainly made a lot of it.'

'*Huevos rancheros?*' Megan said happily. 'I grew up in Arizona. I adore chiles and salsa and fried eggs. And corn meal tortillas? I haven't had any of this stuff in so long . . .' Cam's head sprang up and Megan cursed herself silently. 'I was away from the university for a while,' she said quickly, trying to recover from the slip she'd made, 'doing some research . . . aren't you going to have some of this papaya? It looks delicious.'

'Where did you do your research?' he asked carefully. 'In New York City?'

A faint flush spread over Megan's face. 'You can't do many wildlife studies in New York,' she said pleasantly. 'What makes you think I was there?'

Cam sat down opposite her and leaned back in his chair. 'I don't know,' he said quietly. 'It's just a feeling I have . . . there's something about you, the way you act, the way you talk . . . something almost familiar . . .'

Be careful, Megan warned herself, as her pulse began to race. Be careful of what you say next. He can't possibly make any connection between you and the woman in the alley. It's just that he suspects everyone . . . he's as wary as a fox approaching a hen-house. Say something he doesn't expect, something to throw him off the track . . .

'Don't tell me I picked up a New York accent in only twelve weeks,' she said brightly, forcing a smile to her face. 'You're very perceptive! I was in New York this autumn, taking a seminar with a professor at Columbia University. He's done a study in toxic chemicals, measuring the poison levels absorbed by fatty tissue, and I thought it would be useful to me when I do field autopsies . . . May I pour you some more coffee? Do you want cream or sugar?'

Cam's eyes were fixed on her face with an intensity that frightened her.

'What's his name?' he asked quietly. 'This professor of yours at Columbia—who is he?'

'He's hardly my professor,' Megan said glibly, while she desperately tried to remember the name of someone she'd interviewed two years before while on assignment for *Sophisticate*. 'His name is Jennings,' she said as the long-forgotten name finally flashed into her mind. 'I doubt if you'd have heard of him . . . Did you say you wanted coffee?'

'Why do you keep trying to change the subject?'

Her laughter sounded forced, even to her own ears. 'I'm not trying to change the subject. I just don't think a discussion of Professor Jennings and animal tissues is

terribly interesting, do you? Not in the middle of breakfast on such a beautiful day.'

Cam looked at her thoughtfully over the rim of his
cup. 'It's not this college professor I'm really interested
in. It's you I'm curious about. You see, it's occurred to
me that our meeting as we did was . . . a bit strange. I've
been driving along that same road for years, and until
yesterday, the only other car I've ever seen on it belonged to someone I already knew, someone from a
neighbouring ranch . . . And I still don't know a damned
thing about you,' he added, his eyes narrowing and his
voice dropping slightly. 'Not a damned thing.'

The space between them electrified and became
charged with tension. Cam's suspicions of her were a
ghostly third presence hovering over the small table, and
Megan knew instinctively that she was close to overplay-
ing her hand. There had to be a way to convince him that
she was harmless, that she was not a threat to him. Her
original plan had been to track him to his lair, to watch
and wait and take pictures of him and whomever he
might have secreted away, with a telephoto lens, and
then to ingratiate herself with someone on his household
staff, even bribe them, if necessary, to get the inside
photos and the more intimate details of the mystery that
the man surrounded himself with. Of course, she reminded herself quickly, that had been before she knew
where he lived, before she found out that there were no
hotels, no inns, nothing for as far as she could see but the
endless mountains and grassy mesas. And she had
never, not in her wildest imaginings, expected to be an
overnight guest in his house, breakfasting with him,
answering questions like these.

It was time for a move, she thought desperately, a
bold move, the kind that would surprise him and
yet remove his remaining doubts about her. With

considerable effort, she smiled pleasantly, put down her fork, and extended her hand to him.

'You're right, of course,' she said steadily. 'Here I am, imposing on your hospitality, and I haven't even told you my name. I'm Megan Stevens. I'm sorry I didn't introduce myself last night, but I was a bit muddled, as I'm sure you can understand, Mr Porter.'

He lowered his cup to the table. She held her breath as those famous blue eyes seemed to burn an icy hole through her, keeping the smile on her face until she thought her lips might tremble from the effort, and at last he spoke.

'So you do know who I am,' he murmured. 'Yet, when I asked you that last night . . .'

Megan shrugged her shoulders and lowered her eyes in a way she hoped he'd find naive and appealing.

'I know,' she said hurriedly. 'Isn't that terrible of me? I hope you'll accept my apology . . . You see, I really didn't recognise you at first. It's a little awkward, telling this to someone like you, but meeting you, on the road like that, well, it was just so out of context. I mean, sure, I've seen you on the screen, but to meet a famous American actor on a deserted road in Mexico just doesn't make any sense at all. I mean . . .' She broke off in mid-sentence and looked directly at him. 'That must sound pretty foolish, Mr Porter, but I haven't any other excuse to offer.' Again, she smiled slightly. 'Of course, I promise I'll go to see all your films in the future. How could I do any less, now that I've actually met you?'

Cam studied her in silence. Nothing showed on his face, Megan thought worriedly. His expression was completely neutral, devoid of any reaction to what she had said. Finally, he raised his cup and sipped at the remaining coffee in it.

'That's most thoughtful, Miss Stevens,' he said

tonelessly. 'Tell me, when did this great revelation come
to you? That I was Cameron Porter, I mean. While I was
bringing you here? Or was it some great flash in the
middle of the night?' He set the cup down again and
leaned towards her. 'Or was it, by any chance, not like
that at all? Perhaps you knew who I was even before our
little meeting on the road?'

Easy does it, Megan told herself. He's bitten at the
bait. All you have to do is set the hook properly, and
then reel in the line slowly and carefully. No fast moves
. . . She laughed lightly and, to her pleasure, felt a faint
blush colour her cheeks.

'I'm not sure what you mean, Mr Porter. I told you, I
didn't know who you were at first, but you kept asking
me if I knew who you were . . . and I guess that you
looked sort of familiar. I mean, I kept thinking, why
would he ask me such a question if he wasn't somebody I
should know? Somebody famous. And I said to myself,
well, with those shoulders and that height, he could be a
famous athlete . . .' She smiled charmingly and lowered
her eyes. 'Anyway, it came to me just after Maria
showed me to the guest-room. And believe me, I felt like
an absolute fool. What a dummy you must have thought
I was, Mr Porter.' Hesitantly, eyes wide with innocence,
she looked up at him.

His gaze was still cool, but there was the faint beginning of a smile on his face.

'I see. So if I hadn't asked you if you knew who I was,
you'd never have figured it out.'

'I told you you'd think I was a dummy,' Megan said
quickly. 'I feel especially stupid because only a couple
of weeks ago, I saw you on the Midnight Movie on
television in *Escape from Destiny*. You were terrific!'

She waited breathlessly to see how he would react.
Deliberately, she'd named a ten-year-old film in which

he hadn't appeared, one in which an actor often referred to as his only screen rival had starred. As she watched him, she saw the coolness leave his eyes. His smile, so artificial and controlled only seconds before, broadened into a grin, and she wanted to let out a sigh of relief.

'Thank you,' he said politely. 'I'm glad you approved.'

'I don't know much about acting,' she said innocently, all the while thinking that clearly she did, that hers was an award-winning performance, if only he knew it, 'but I do know when someone does a good job. And you certainly did one in that film.'

'That's nice to hear, Miss Stevens. And what about you? Are you good at your job?'

'Am I good . . .?' Megan stammered and raised her eyes to his. 'I don't follow you.'

'Are you a good biologist? I take it you think this project of yours will make you better at your job.'

'Oh,' she said, fighting against the desire to burst into laughter, 'yes, I'm sure it will. There must be lots of animals for me to survey here. Didn't you say last night there were lots of cats in these mountains?'

Cam nodded his head and smiled. 'Lots. And grizzlies, of course, and wolves and coyotes . . . you'll have your hands full. What are you particularly interested in studying?'

'Everything,' she said airily. 'Habitat, and food sources, and denning and whatever.'

He frowned slightly and his smile dimmed. 'That's pretty broad, isn't it? I didn't think field studies were done that way.'

'This isn't a sanctioned study,' Megan said quickly. 'I just need some data to use in my thesis, and my professor suggested this area.' She turned away from him and looked out towards the rolling hills and mountain peaks rising majestically from the mist-shrouded grass of the mesa. 'This place is perfect, just perfect. If only I could stay here for a couple of days . . . just long enough to sketch out some initial ideas . . .'

He got to his feet so suddenly that she was startled. She looked up at him in surprise, afraid she had pressed him too far.

'Unfortunately, you may have to do just that,' he said, his voice no longer quite so pleasant. 'So far, I haven't been able to make any arrangements for you or your car.'

It was difficult to control the sudden elation she felt as she heard his words.

'You mean you haven't found someone to come for my car?'

'I haven't been able to reach the garage yet. We're very isolated up here, Miss Stevens . . .'

'Call me Megan,' she said quickly.

'Megan, then,' he said somewhat stiffly. 'There are no telephone lines.'

'No telephone lines? But last night, you said . . .'

'I said I'd call for someone to pick you up and tow your car to a garage. I have a ham radio, you see. I use it to reach someone in the valley who places any necessary phone calls for me. It's rather complicated, but it works most of the time.'

'Most of the time?' she echoed blankly.

Cam nodded. 'This isn't New York, you know. The phone lines go out every now and then, and my friend tells me that's what's happened, but you needn't worry —I'm sure that they'll be repaired by tomorrow.'

'I'm not worried,' she said quickly, trying to conceal her delight. 'I was just wondering if you don't find living like this a little inconvenient?'

He smiled so openly and with such contentment that Megan was amazed at the transformation.

'Never,' he said positively. 'You'd be surprised at how quickly you learn that a telephone is rarely an asset and almost always an annoyance. I've managed more than nicely without one. Doing without electricity is much harder, believe me.'

'But there were lights on in the house last night . . .'

Cam grinned at her. 'I told you it was harder to do without electricity. After a couple of years of living by candlelight, I finally gave in and installed a generator.'

'You've had this place for some time, then?'

The smile vanished from his face and a polite, closed look took its place as he pushed his chair back towards the table.

'I'll try placing the calls later this afternoon. Meanwhile, I have work to do. Please ask Maria for anything you need.' He turned and started down the steps leading off the patio and Megan rose to her feet, desperately trying to think of some way to detain him. Suddenly, he turned back towards her. 'And by the way, I suggest you stay near the house. I know you're a biologist, but I'm not at all convinced you're really prepared for how wild and dangerous these mountains can be. I'd hate to have to come to your rescue a second time.'

'A second time?' she repeated. 'That's not fair . . . that accident last night wasn't my fault . . .'

Her indignant voice rose as he strode away from the house without answering her. Megan watched him as he walked towards a stand of trees and disappeared from view. She waited to make sure that he wasn't going to reappear, and then she leaped to her feet and hurried into the house, determined to get a closer look at it and take some photos if she could. Without even trying, she'd gained an incredible opportunity. In fact, this entire situation was incredible. Whatever she had expected to find in Mexico, it wasn't anything like this. Who could have imagined the famous Cameron Porter living in such isolation, cut off from the world in such a magnificent, rugged wilderness? No telephone? she thought with amazement. And what had he said? That he'd spent a couple of years without electricity? She shook her head in disbelief as she reached the guest-room. Well, if he did have a secret, this was the perfect place to hide it.

She snatched up her camera and tucked an extra roll of film in the pocket of her denim jacket. What a scoop this would be, she thought with excitement. Her article, her photos, would be a first. Suddenly, it struck her that photos of the interior of his home would be far easier to get than pictures of him. He was the story, and he was out there, somewhere in those mountains. Hastily, she left her room and hurried towards the other end of the house.

'Maria? Are you there? Maria? Oh, there you are,' Megan said, smiling at the housekeeper. 'I was wondering . . . where has the *Señor* gone, do you know? I . . . I forgot to ask him something.'

The woman smiled and placed her hands on her ample hips. 'Where he always goes, the first day he returns to Las Montanas en Cielo. That is the name of this ranch, *Señorita*,' she explained when Megan looked puzzled. 'He calls it Mountains in the Sky. A proper name, *sí*?'

'*Sí*, Maria, it is indeed. But where does he always go?'

Maria turned to the huge picture window behind her and pointed out towards a snow-topped peak.

'There,' she said simply. 'There is where he goes always.'

'He's gone up the mountain, you mean. I see . . .'

The housekeeper nodded and started back towards the kitchen.

'One other thing,' Megan said quickly. 'Is he alone,

Maria? I mean, this is such a big house . . . I thought perhaps there might be someone else living here.'

Maria's dark eyes slid away from Megan. 'There is no one else here now, *Señorita*,' she murmured finally. 'No one but the *Señor*.' She looked up and cocked her head to the side. 'He is a nice man, *Señorita*, is he not?'

Megan looked at the housekeeper in surprise. 'Why, yes, yes, he seems to be.'

The woman studied her in silence and then smiled. 'The stable is behind the house, *Señorita*. Tell Miguel I have sent you and to give you a fine horse.' Her smile widened and she dropped her voice to a whisper. 'If you hurry, *Señorita*, you can catch up with the *Señor*.' Megan nodded her thanks and started for the foyer, but the housekeeper's voice called her back. '*Señorita* . . . I am glad *Señor* Porter brought you to this house. Perhaps, soon, he will be glad, too.'

Megan nodded again. She could think of nothing appropriate to say, and, as she looked into Maria's honest, open face, she felt a faint twinge of shame.

CHAPTER FOUR

MEGAN held the reins in one hand while she patted her horse's neck reassuringly with the other. The grey Arabian tossed her head and snorted softly as she picked her way delicately along the narrow, shadowed path leading up the mountain. Megan had followed Maria's directions to the tree-shaded stone stables. There, using a combination of broken Spanish and hand signals, she'd finally persuaded a young man with dark eyes and a shy smile to bring out the grey filly and help her mount. When she asked where *Señor* Porter had gone, he'd pointed towards the mountain peak that towered over the house.

The sun had burned off the last remaining wisps of morning fog, but once she had ridden into the tall pines that stood like alert sentinels along the mountain's curved flank, the sunlight seemed to vanish. The trail leading upwards wound through the trees like a snake coiling lazily through high grass. Heavy branches of dark green pine needles hung low overhead, blocking out the light and deadening the sound of the horse's hooves. Nothing marred the silence except the occasional cry of a bird from deep within the towering pines.

It was cool and eerie in the forest, and Megan shivered in spite of the heavy wool sweater she'd tossed on over her shirt. There was a sudden flash of beige and brown as something skittered across the trail and the filly tossed her head nervously, blowing loudly through her nostrils as she caught its scent. How easy it would be to get lost among these trees, Megan thought with a twinge of fear. In a place as wild and remote as this, anything was possible. She had not known quite what to expect when she first followed Cam Porter from the airport at Durango. A quick look at a couple of guidebooks had prepared her for an area that was mountainous and beautiful, a place of deep canyons, high waterfalls, and good hunting. She'd formed a hazy picture of Cam living in a handsome lodge set in a carefully manicured clearing among a stand of well-pruned trees, a kind of chic, expensive hideaway that boasted all the trappings of luxury, complete with pool, servants and fawning admirers. Nothing she'd imagined had prepared her for the primitive splendour and isolation of this place.

The horse snorted again and tossed its head as a crow suddenly swooped from the trees and dropped low over the trail ahead. It plucked something from the dust and then flew away, its glossy black wings beating rapidly as it fought to regain height. Megan's eyes followed the bird as it flew towards the trees ahead, and suddenly she was gazing up into blue sky and bright sunlight. With a sense of relief, she urged the horse forwards.

The pines ended almost abruptly, as did the narrow trail. Ahead, like a brilliant emerald carpet leading to the upper reaches of the mountain, stretched a grassy meadow. A horse and its rider were silhouetted against the peak and, even from a distance, Megan knew it was Cam. He looked as he had in some of his films—broadshouldered, dark-haired, sitting in the saddle with relaxed, masculine grace, but with an ease about him that the camera never quite caught. His shoulders seemed to strain against the confines of his wool shirt. He raised his hand and pulled off a sweat-darkened, sun-faded, wide-brimmed Stetson hat, and ran his hand through his dark hair in a gesture she remembered from some of his films. There was an exciting virility in him, even at this distance, and she hesitated, caught up momentarily in an unwanted and surprising sense of pleasure as she watched him.

'Come on, Megan,' she whispered to herself. 'Get back to work.' Quickly, she touched her heels to her horse's flanks and headed towards him.

'You seem determined to follow me everywhere,' he said as she rode up beside him. 'I thought I told you to stay close to the house.'

She smiled pleasantly, deliberately ignoring the look of displeasure on his face. 'It's such a beautiful day . . . I just couldn't resist getting outdoors for a while. Maria said you'd be riding up the mountain.'

Cam clucked softly to his horse and the animal moved forwards at a slow walk.

'Maria talks too much,' he muttered. 'And Miguel should have known better than to saddle a horse for you.'

'It wasn't his fault,' Megan said quickly, falling in place beside him. 'I told him that it would be all right. It is, isn't it? I mean, I know how to ride—you don't have to worry about me.'

He glanced over at her and scowled. 'It seems to me I haven't had much choice about that ever since yesterday, have I?'

His horse was moving faster, trotting across the green meadow towards a wall of rock near the base of the mountain, and Megan spurred the filly slightly and drew abreast of him.

'This is magnificent country,' she said pleasantly, determined not to be drawn into a quarrel. 'Would you mind if I rode along with you?'

'As a matter of fact, I would. Playing the role of good Samaritan last night was enough; I don't want to spend the next few hours nursing you along.'

Her hands tightened on the reins and she glanced over at him. 'That's an unfair remark,' she said quickly. 'I can ride as well as you can . . .'

'I doubt that.'

'. . . and I don't need looking after. I darned near grew up on a horse.'

He looked at her and frowned. 'For someone who grew up on a horse, you should know better than to try to ride wearing those shoes.'

Megan flushed and glanced down at her feet. 'They'll do. They're hiking boots.'

'I know what they are,' he said curtly. 'They're made of canvas and leather, and they're no better for hiking in these mountains than they are for riding. For your sake, I hope the rest of your equipment is more suitable than that. When you leave here later today . . .'

Her spirits sank at the sound of his words. 'Later today? Then your friend in the village was able to make that call?'

'No, not yet,' he admitted, and she breathed a silent prayer of gratitude to whomever was responsible for fixing the telephone lines. 'But I'm sure he'll be able to get through later. At least your car is off the road. Miguel and I drove down at dawn and towed it to the side with the Land Rover.'

Megan nodded her head and forced a polite smile to her face. 'Thank you,' she said. 'I guess I'm in your debt again. How can I ever repay you for all you've done?'

'For starters, you can go back to the house,' he growled. 'You're slowing me down.'

'You needn't take it easy on my account. I can keep up . . .'

He glanced over at her and smiled slightly. 'Suit yourself,' he said, spurring his horse into a gallop.

'Hey . . . wait . . .'

But Cam was already moving rapidly away from her, heading towards the rocky outcropping at the base of the mountain. Megan hesitated only briefly before following.

It had been a couple of years since she'd ridden, but she fell easily into the old, familiar feeling of letting her body assume the rhythm of the galloping animal beneath her. The Arabian was swift-moving and sure-footed, and the hand-tooled Western saddle was the kind she was used to. She glanced down for a second and sighed. Although she would never admit it to him, she knew Cam had been right about her hiking shoes. Leather boots, with the right kind of heel for placement in the steel stirrups that dangled from the saddle, would have made her feel more secure as the horse flew across the meadow. Well, she thought, they would have to do. The important thing was to keep up with Cam, to spend the little time left here observing him . . . if he gave her the chance. He seemed determined to rebuff all her attempts at polite conversation. No matter, she thought grimly. He could be as rude and surly as he liked. She was going to stick to his side like a burr on a horse until the second she had to leave. The only way he'd be able to get rid of her would be to vanish into thin air . . . and he had! Megan blinked in astonishment. It wasn't possible . . . she had taken her eyes off him for a couple of seconds and he'd simply disappeared from sight. Slowing the horse to a walk, she peered all around her, but there was nothing to be seen in any direction except for the waving grass and the rocks ahead.

'Hello,' she called out, her voice tentative and faltering in the silence. 'Cam? Where are you?'

As if in answer, there was a faint whinny from ahead. The Arabian pricked her ears and snorted softly. Megan loosened her hold on the reins, letting the animal move forwards unguided as it picked its way towards the wall of rock. At the last second, just as it seemed as if the horse was going to collide with the massive obstacle, a narrow passage appeared in the outcropping. The filly headed for the hidden opening without hesitating, and Megan looked up in surprise as high walls of rough sandstone loomed up on either side. She leaned down and stroked the Arabian's neck.

'Good girl,' she whispered. 'I guess you knew this canyon was here all the time, hmm? I never would have found it without you. But where's your owner gone to? He's got to be here somewhere . . .'

She broke off in mid-sentence as a sudden movement at the far end of the canyon caught her eye. A herd of horses, their coats gleaming in the bright sunlight, was grazing contentedly in the tall grass. A few hundred yards away, Cam sat motionless in his saddle, watching them. Slowly, Megan moved forward and drew to a halt near him.

'Don't make any sudden movements,' he said in a low voice. 'Those animals can move like the wind if they get spooked.'

'They're magnificent,' Megan whispered. 'Are they yours?'

He nodded his head and smiled. 'As much as they can be anybody's,' he murmured. 'Beautiful, aren't they?'

'Oh, yes, they certainly are. It's hard to tell from this distance . . . they look like Arabians.'

'Every last one of them,' he said softly. 'The most handsome animals in the world. And the hardiest.'

Megan nodded in agreement. 'That's what my Dad always said. He sold his soul for a black Arabian stud and bred it to some of our purebreds . . . a few of our neighbours thought he was crazy, but the foals he got were really tough and adaptable.' She shaded her eyes with her hand and frowned. 'Is it the sunlight, or are there lots of Palominos in that herd?'

'It's not the light,' he said, glancing at her in surprise. 'You really do know something about horses, don't you?'

'I told you I was raised on a ranch,' she answered quickly. 'And how could anybody not recognise that wonderful colour? They look as if they were dipped in gold.'

'Yes, but not everybody knows it's a colour, not a breed.' He looked at her again and smiled. 'Strange, isn't it? The Spaniards came to Mexico and damned near tore the country apart, looking for a hoard of gold that wasn't here . . . and left behind the only gold worth having. The Palomino,' he explained, when Megan looked puzzled. 'Cortez gave a golden horse to one of his lieutenants, Juan de Palomino, more than four hundred years ago. That was the beginning of all of this.'

She smiled back at him, amazed by how relaxed and pleasant he suddenly seemed. 'You're the one who knows about horses,' she said softly. 'I'm kind of surprised.'

The grin faded from his face, replaced by a wary frown. 'Why?' he demanded. 'Why should you be surprised?'

She shrugged her shoulders and shook her head. 'I don't know,' she lied, carefully looking away from him. 'I just thought . . . Well, if someone had told me Cam Porter owned a herd of Arabians on a ranch in the middle of the Sierra Madre Mountains, I wouldn't have believed him.'

'What would you have believed? That Cam Porter owned a string of polo ponies? That he owned a mansion in Hollywood? That he spent his time sailing a yacht in the Mediterranean? Or is it that you would have preferred believing those things?'

She blushed as she thought how close to the truth he was. 'That's not fair,' she said quickly. 'I simply said . . .'

He sighed and shook his head. 'Yeah, I know. Forget it.'

'All I meant was . . .'

Cam held his hand up and cut her off. 'Look, I was wrong,' he said gruffly. 'I'm sorry if I over-reacted. It's just that everybody seems to have lots of preconceived ideas about what I am, and I . . .' An embarrassed smile tugged at the corners of his mouth and he broke off in mid-sentence. 'Anyway, I can't lay the blame for that on you. You aren't responsible for that awful stuff they publish about me.'

To her surprise, Megan blushed with discomfort. 'No,' she said stiffly, the taste of the lie strangely bitter on her tongue, 'no, I'm not.' She glanced over at him and caught her lower lip between her teeth. 'Perhaps they print lies because they don't know the truth.'

'They'd print lies even if they did,' he said quickly. 'It doesn't matter anyway.'

'But . . .'

'I said it doesn't matter,' he repeated sharply. His horse tossed its head and whinnied softly, and Cam ran a reassuring hand along the animal's neck. 'The wind's shifted,' he murmured. 'The horses smell something. Do you think you can find your way back to the house alone? I want to check what's spooking them.'

Megan took a deep breath. 'I could,' she admitted, 'but I'd really like to come along with you. I promise, I won't get in the way.'

He hesitated and then, to her surprise, he nodded. 'Why not? At least that way I won't have to worry about whether or not you get lost going back.'

'Lost?' she repeated indignantly. 'I got here without any trouble, didn't I?'

But she was talking to empty space. With a sigh, she urged her horse after his. The man was a puzzle, she thought, as she galloped after him. In fact, he was impossible to classify. First, he'd run her off the road and then he'd come back to rescue her. She was an uninvited intruder in his home, yet he treated her with tolerant politeness. She thought of the pride with which he'd spoken of his horses, the bitter words he'd used to describe the kind of things people assumed he did, and again that discomforting twinge of guilt stirred inside her. She shook her head and frowned, annoyed at herself. Owning a herd of horses and making impassioned speeches didn't change anything, she reminded herself sternly. The Arabians were no more than a rich man's expensive hobby, and as for the things he'd said . . . the man was an actor. He could probably read the telephone directory aloud and stir an audience. With a faint smile, she began to draft the opening line of her feature article:

'Cameron Porter's favourite acting role is the one he assumes in the Sierra Madre Mountains of Mexico, where he plays at being a rancher in a private, macho world . . .'

. . . A world his wife must have hated, she thought. The handsome house, the grazing herd, the magnificent countryside . . . It was probably the ultimate Hollywood set, not a real ranch like the one on which she'd been raised. She doubted if Cam ever did anything more strenuous than ride his horse. As for his talk of cats and grizzlies . . . Megan smiled to herself. The wild-cat they'd seen the night before was probably a rare intruder. A Hollywood cowboy wouldn't live in a

place where there was anything much larger or more
dangerous than a rabbit prowling the grounds.

'Megan!' Her head snapped up and she trotted up to
where he waited for her. 'Vultures,' he said, pointing to
half a dozen black, spiralling shapes in the sky. 'You'd
better wait here while I find out what they're after.'

'I'm coming with you,' she called, as he touched his
heels to his horse's flanks and galloped through the
canyon.

Several dark, feathered shapes rose heavily from the
grass as they approached, reluctant to leave the bloodied
form sprawled on the ground. Cam swung down from
the saddle and bent beside what remained of a grey colt.
He looked up at Megan as she pulled up alongside.

'A puma did this,' he said shortly. 'One of those cats
you came here to study. This isn't a very pretty sight,
Megan. I don't think you want to see it.'

'I've seen dead things before,' she said quietly, kneeling down beside him. The colt's eyes were open, milky
and opaque with death. This was all too real, Megan
thought uncomfortably, swallowing past the bitter taste
in her mouth. She looked away from the gaping wound
in the animal's throat and watched as Cam ran his hand
gently along the animal's flank.

'Poor little guy,' he murmured at last. 'He didn't stand
a chance.'

She looked at him across the stiffened body, wanting
to say something to ease the pain she saw in his eyes.

'At least it was quick,' she said finally, forcing herself
to look back at the colt's neck. 'Better than dying slowly
of exhaustion or illness. There was probably something
wrong with it, Cam.'

He laughed bitterly as he ran his hand along the
animal's rump. 'If there wasn't, there sure as hell is now.
Damn that cat . . .'

'The cat has to survive,' Megan answered quickly. 'You eat meat, don't you? Well, so does he. And I'll bet anything you like that this colt was slow or weak . . . Predators are pretty selective about their prey.'

Cam got to his feet slowly. 'I know you're right,' he said finally. 'But I spent a lot of time with this guy . . . he wasn't very strong. We kept him and the mare corralled near the stables longer than usual. He seemed weak and unsteady his first few months, although there didn't seem to be any reason for it.'

Megan sighed and patted the dead colt. 'You see? There was something wrong. That's usually the way it is.' She stroked the animal one last time and then stood up. 'Still, it's hard to see something die that way—it hurts, even when you understand the reason.'

He took the coiled rope hanging from the horn of his saddle and knelt next to the colt again. 'I'm·going to move him away from these mesquite bushes,' he said, throwing a line around the stiffened legs and drawing them together with an expert hitch. 'Either Andres or I will have to come up here tonight and wait for the cat that did this to return.'

'Andres?' Megan repeated.

Cam nodded as he swung up into the saddle and clucked softly to his horse. 'My foreman,' he explained, as he rode slowly towards open ground.

She took hold of her horse's trailing reins and walked to where he'd dismounted.

'So this . . . Andres . . . runs the ranch for you?'

'Only when I'm not around,' he said, loosening the rope and looping it back into a coil.

Megan watched his strong, slightly calloused fingers as they worked the rope. 'What do you do when you're around?'

A wry grin flickered across his face. 'What do I do? I

ride, I rope, I brand foals and fix fences, and do whatever other work needs doing.' As he grasped the reins of his horse his smile broadened. 'What did you think I did? Sat on the terrace and sipped tequila?'

She flushed and looked away from him. 'What will you do about the puma?' she asked quickly, afraid the answer to the question he'd asked was visible on her face.

'Get rid of it,' he answered. 'These hills are home to lots of predators. Your puma . . .'

She arched her eyebrows and stared at him quizzically. 'It's hardly my puma.'

'Your puma,' he repeated deliberately, 'to say nothing of wolves and coyotes . . . and other things.'

Megan walked along beside him, trying to keep pace with his long strides. 'Yes,' she said evenly, 'you mentioned grizzlies.'

'It wasn't bears I had in mind. There are bandits in these hills, too.'

In spite of herself, she burst out laughing. 'Come on, Cam. Bandits? In this day and age? You've got me half-believing you about the grizzlies, but bandits?'

He shrugged his shoulders. 'Grizzlies and bandits both,' he insisted. 'Robbers, rebels, drug-dealers—they've all turned up in the Sierra Madres at one time or another. If I were you, I'd head back to Durango and take the first plane out.'

'Why?' she demanded. 'Because you say so?'

His eyes moved slowly over her, travelling from her face to her feet with such deliberate insolence that she felt herself blushing.

'That's one good reason,' he said quietly. 'The other is fairly self-evident.'

Again, those blue eyes raked over her. She felt as if her cheeks were blazing with colour, but she forced herself to return his stare.

'You mean I should leave because I'm a woman, don't you?'

'I'd say the same thing to anybody, man or woman, who came into these mountains knowing as little about them as you do. But you're right—being a woman puts you at a special disadvantage.'

'It won't matter to the animals,' she said stiffly. 'And I don't believe a word you said about bandits. Anyway, I can take care of myself.' She looked away from him, adding with studied casualness, 'You'll see that for yourself when I set up camp.'

'I'm afraid you won't get the chance,' he said calmly. 'You'd need my permission to camp anywhere near here, and you might as well know I won't give it.'

'Your permission?' she repeated incredulously. 'Yesterday, you acted as if you owned the road. Don't tell me—now, you're going to say you own these mountains.'

'Not all of them,' he said with a faint smile. 'But I do own all the land you can cover in a two-day ride. This is a working ranch, Megan. There's no room on it for a woman setting herself up for trouble.'

'You're very sure of yourself, aren't you? I mean, the message is clear: you have work to do, but I'm just fooling around, wasting time.'

'I didn't say that,' he said mildly.

'Yes, you did,' she insisted, amazed that she could have felt compassion for him only moments before. 'This is a working ranch,' she mimicked unpleasantly. 'And I'm a woman setting herself up for trouble.'

'Those are simple facts, Megan. You know nothing about these hills. You didn't even know enough to rent the proper kind of car. Now you refuse to admit that bandits might have . . . special interest in coming across a woman alone out here. Yes, you're setting yourself up for trouble.'

'Then let me camp on your land,' she said quickly. 'That would be safe, wouldn't it?'

He laughed and turned away from her, leading his horse carefully over the rocky bottom of a dry stream bed.

'I own the land,' he said. 'That doesn't mean I can guarantee your safety. If you don't believe me, just go back and take another look at that colt. The only way you'd be safe is if I spent most of my time checking up on you, and I have other things to do.'

She quickened her pace, trying to catch up to him, hurrying along the tumbled rocks as he moved further and further away from her.

'I wouldn't be any bother,' she called to his retreating back, trying to keep the desperation from her voice, knowing that if what he said was true, if all the land she could see was his, it would be impossible for her to find a way to set up camp and spy on him. 'Maybe I could find that cat for you . . . there are ways to chase them out of an area . . .'

The ring of his laughter mocked her as he swung into his saddle. 'How?' he called. 'With a container of hairspray?'

'Dammit, Cameron Porter . . . You come back here! Weren't you the one who made that whole speech about being pre-judged?' she yelled after him as he cantered away. 'That's just what you're doing to me . . . Can't you wait a minute? This area is perfect for my field study . . . It's . . .'

Megan ducked instinctively as a shadowy form swooped overhead and the harsh sound of rustling feathers filled the air. It was one of the vultures, returning to its interrupted meal. The Arabian shied, dragging the reins through Megan's fingers, and, as she lurched after them, her foot jammed between two loose rocks in the dry stream bed. She cried out as a sharp pain lanced through her ankle and the frightened horse skittered off and then galloped in the direction Cam had taken.

Gingerly, Megan put her weight down on her foot. She winced slightly, then sighed with relief. Her ankle hurt, but she was sure nothing was broken. The sound of her horse's hoofbeats faded gradually into the silence of the meadow. 'Damn!' she muttered. It was going to be a long, hard walk back to the ranch. And if Cam had been telling the truth about bears . . . She took a deep breath and squared her shoulders. No bear in its right mind would come near a human being, she told herself. Still, it might not be a bad idea to whistle or sing as she walked, to make some noise just to announce her presence . . . She walked a few steps and winced again. If only the arrogant fool hadn't ridden off like that . . .

She knelt down and relaced her shoes, hoping that if she tightened them, she might have better footing for the long hike ahead. As she bent her head, a dark shadow appeared on the grass before her. She gasped and leaped to her feet, mouth dry and pulse racing, as the shadow lenghtened until, with a sigh of relief, she realised it was Cam riding towards her.

'Are you all right?' he demanded, leaping from the saddle. 'What happened?'

'I just turned my ankle a little,' she said quickly. 'I'm okay.'

'Are you sure?' he insisted, a harsh stridency in his voice.

She shook her head and blinked back the sudden unexpected feeling of tears threatening to spill down her cheeks.

'I'm positive. Really. My horse shied and . . .' She

paused and waited until her voice was calmer. 'What made you come back?'

He knelt beside her and unlaced her shoe. 'Your horse came flying down the trail behind me,' he said roughly. 'Only problem was, you weren't on it. Does this hurt?' he asked, flexing her foot carefully. She shook her head and he flexed it in the other direction. 'How about this?' Again, she shook her head.

He ran his fingers over her ankle, his touch as gentle and soft as it had been when he stroked the dead colt.

'It's my fault,' he said gruffly. 'I shouldn't have left you behind. I told you it wasn't safe . . .'

'It was just a clumsy accident, Cam. I could have done the same thing to my ankle walking down the street. It just feels a little tender when I stand on it.' Suddenly, the situation and all its possibilities struck her, and she smiled tentatively at him. 'I'm sure I'll be fine after a couple of days.'

'I'm sure you will be,' he said at once, retying the laces. 'Anyway, there's a doctor in Durango. As soon as you get back there, have him check your ankle for you.'

Megan's smile faltered. 'I thought perhaps . . .'

'You thought wrong,' he said. 'Now, give me your hand.'

Defiantly, she pulled away from his outstretched hand and got to her feet. Anger made her move too quickly, and suddenly she moaned and bit down on her lip. Cam's arm went around her and he pulled her against him before she could fall.

'Why the hell are you so damned stubborn?' he said angrily. 'Do you have to do everything your way?'

'I don't need your help,' she answered coldly, trying unsuccessfully to break free of his encircling arm. 'I can manage by myself . . .'

He swept her up into his arms and strode towards his

horse. 'Do you make it a practice to be an idiot at least once a day?' he growled. 'There's no way you can walk back down this mountain on that ankle.'

It was pointless to argue. He was right—she knew that without question. Humiliation swept over her, and embarrassment . . . and something else. Her cheek was pressed against his rough wool shirt; she could hear the steady beat of his heart under her ear, feel the muscles in his arms tensing as they held her tightly against him. He smelled of the sun and the horse and the grass in the meadow, a combination somehow far more pleasant and more intimate than any cologne. Her face was so close to his neck that she could see the dark, curling hair in the open neck of his shirt. Quickly, Megan closed her eyes. Once, standing on a high, swaying rope bridge, looking down into the tumbling rapids far below, she'd felt this same sort of dizziness, a feeling of vertigo born of fascination and fear . . . It made no sense. Perhaps she'd injured her ankle more than she'd realised . . .

'Megan? What is it?'

Her eyes flew open and met Cam's.

'It's . . . it's nothing,' she murmured, blushing under the intensity of his gaze. 'I just felt a little faint . . . You can put me down now,' she said more firmly.

For the span of a heartbeat, his arms seemed to tighten around her. Then, in one swift motion, he lifted her up into the saddle.

'Hold on to the pommel,' he ordered, and she obeyed almost meekly. He swung up behind her and she stiffened instinctively, trying to avoid making contact with him. 'If you fall off,' he said threateningly, 'I'm not coming back for you. Lean back against me, Megan. And, for God's sake, try to relax.'

It was impossible not to do as he said. There was no way to sit separate and apart, and finally she leaned back against his chest and gave herself up to the swaying motion of the horse and the protective warmth of his encircling arms. She could feel his breath against her cheek and the occasional rough rasp of his chin against her face as she shifted her body in vain, trying to limit the contact between them.

It was no wonder he was a star on almost every continent, she thought dizzily. The strength and masculinity he exuded on screen was real, not the creation of a director or producer. And he was definitely the most handsome man she'd ever known, she admitted to herself, as he shifted in the saddle and pulled her more firmly back against him. Not handsome in the traditional way—Cam's features were too sharply defined and chiselled for that—but in a way that suggested a kind of restrained inner resolve, the same resolve she felt in the tautly muscled arms that held her.

What was he thinking? she wondered. He'd said she would be nothing but trouble, and so far, she'd proved him right. Was he counting the minutes until he could get rid of her? He was such a strange man, she thought. Gentle one minute, gruff the next . . . She was always quick to understand the people she wrote about, but Cam kept eluding her. And why these persistent feelings of guilt? She'd pulled off the greatest coup a journalist could hope for—with his unwitting help—and yet . . . She closed her eyes, and again she saw herself standing on that swaying bridge.

'Megan?' he said softly. She thought she felt his hand brush her cheek, and her eyes flew open. 'We're back.'

He slid from the saddle and stood looking up at her, an unfathomable expression on his face. He raised his arms and grasped her waist, lifting her down from the horse. As her hands touched his shoulders, the vertigo came over her again and she swayed towards him. Everything around her had the unfocused softness of a dream and she felt vulnerable and exposed when her eyes met his. Her feet touched the ground and still he held her, until suddenly the horse nuzzled her and they stepped apart.

'I'll get Miguel to help you into the house.'

She nodded her head and lowered her eyes. 'Yes, all right,' she whispered.

He took hold of the horse's bridle and then turned back to her. 'Why in hell are you here?' he demanded, and she shrank back from the anger in his voice.

'I told you . . . I have a study to do.'

'You can't stay here, Megan,' he whispered in a rough, strained voice. 'It's impossible.'

Again, she nodded and this time her eyes met his. He'd never know how right he was, she thought in amazement. It was, indeed, impossible.

CHAPTER FIVE

THE long afternoon was fading into evening. From her bedroom window, where she sat in a comfortable armchair, Megan watched the snow-capped mountains as they blushed pinkly beneath the gentle kiss of the setting sun. Her leg was propped on a footstool, the ankle carefully wrapped in an elastic bandage. She glanced down at the open book in her lap, then sighed, closed it and set it on the table next to her.

Cam had brought the footstool to her room after carefully bandaging her ankle, in spite of her protests that it was fine, that it barely hurt. He'd been polite but abrupt, almost curt. She knew the reason, of course: he'd told her that the telephone lines were still out. It took no great effort on her part to imagine how he felt, trapped into yet another night of having to permit the intrusion of a stranger in his home. She had greater difficulty understanding her own feelings. Ever since the ride back from the canyon meadow, she'd felt strangely disorientated. She knew what was happening—she was losing her objectivity about him—because it had happened to her once before, when she was researching a story on abandoned children. But it had been understandable then, and it added a compassionate reality to her article when she wrote it. Well, she assured herself, she had enough information on Cam to write a terrific article. Not quite the sort she and Marian had planned, but one that would sell magazines. It was time to make some last minute notes on her tape recorder, take a few more photos, and get out.

She'd spent the last hour reading. Cam had been the polite, solicitous host, suggesting she ask Maria to show her to the library so she could find something to help her pass the time. He reminded her that there was aspirin in the guest bathroom and that she was to feel free to call the housekeeper for anything else she might need. The entire conversation had been conducted with the greatest civility and formality, but she could tell that it was difficult for him—his eyes never met hers while they spoke, and he left the room as soon as he was satisfied that she was comfortable. How could you dislike a man who had sheltered a stranger, cared for her, and remained polite even when that stranger had clearly overstayed her welcome?

Slowly, holding on to the table for support, Megan got to her feet, putting her weight on the injured ankle with the greatest care. Except for a slight twinge, it seemed fine. Favouring it slightly, she moved to the massive dresser across the room and looked through the books she'd stacked upon it earlier. Cam's library had turned out to be a small, cosy room lined with ceiling-to-floor bookcases. Most of the books had the well thumbed, worn look of things read many times over, purchased for their contents and not simply to fill shelves and impress others. There was hardly any contemporary fiction but a great variety of almost everything else: books on philosophy were tucked in next to histories, and psychology texts fought Shakespeare and Ibsen for space. There was an entire half-wall of books about horses, and two shelves held nothing but slim volumes of poetry. The room, and the books in it, were like him, she'd thought as she made her selections: workmanlike yet handsome, not at all easy to categorise, and complex in the variety of interests they revealed.

Picking up a first edition of T. S. Eliot, she hobbled

back to her chair, but it was impossible to concentrate on the imagery and rhythm of Eliot's poems. By this time next week, her article would be completed and ready for the next issue of *Sophisticate*. Her words would transport millions of readers into Cam Porter's private domain, and this secret kingdom of his would no longer be quite so insulated from the rest of the world. And there would be plenty of photos to go along with the feature: Maria, eager to get back to whatever it was that smelled so delicious as it cooked in the kitchen, had been happy to leave Megan alone in the library, and she'd pulled her camera from her pocket and snapped off several shots, even risking a few as she'd gone back to the guest-room, so that now she had pictures of virtually every room in the house, except, of course, for Cam's bedroom. Marian would be satisfied . . . she'd uncovered no great secrets about his marriage or his wife's death, but her article would still be unique. She shifted uneasily in the chair and ran her hand across her forehead. Why, then, this awful feeling of unhappiness? And what on earth had come over her on that dream-like, interminable ride back to the ranch?

There was a dull, echoing noise from outside the house. Megan parted the coarse burlap curtains and peered out of the window. Near the corner of a corral she could see Cam, shirtless in the weak, late afternoon light, hammering a new post into the long line of split-rail fencing that stretched towards the stables. There were two vaqueros working alongside him and as she watched, he turned to one of them and said something. The three men laughed and one of them nodded and handed Cam a leather wineskin. He tipped his head back and squeezed it until a dark red stream of liquid spurted into his mouth. With a grin, he tossed the wineskin aside, then picked up the sledgehammer again and drove the post into the ground. The ease with which he swung the hammer, the way the muscles in his arms and back responded to the effort, made it clear that he was accustomed to work of this sort. His was not the artificially muscled body of the men she saw all too often on the streets of New York City, where every male of the right age and social background seemed to have had himself moulded to perfect order on an exercise machine. Cam was lean, narrow through the waist and hips, and the musculature of his upper body and arms was obviously the result of hard outdoor work. She could still remember the feel of his arms as they'd closed around her . . .

Megan shook her head irritably and snapped the curtains closed. What on earth was wrong with her? Earlier this afternoon, if he had put her in his Land Rover and driven her back to Durango, she probably wouldn't even have protested. 'You can't stay here, Megan,' he'd said, 'it's impossible,' and she'd been only too ready to agree for reasons far different from his. And there was no denying the discomfort she'd felt snapping photos of his house just a short while ago. Now, here she was, watching him from behind the curtains, mooning over the way he'd held her on the ride back to the ranch . . .

'You're behaving like a schoolgirl,' she whispered aloud. 'What kind of behaviour is this, for heaven's sake?' Taking a deep breath, she reached for her camera. Marian would love some shots showing Cam at work on his ranch, and these would be terrific. And how she'd laugh when she heard all the details of the past couple of days, especially how Cam had almost mesmerised Megan. It would make an amusing story to tell during a long, lazy luncheon when she returned to the city.

'*Señorita?*'

Megan started at the tap on the door and the soft sound of Maria's voice. '*Momentito*,' she called, stalling for time while she tucked the camera away out of sight. 'Yes, Maria. What is it?'

'You are feeling well, *Señorita*?' the housekeeper asked, smiling at her from the doorway.

'Yes, thank you, I'm fine.'

'*Bueno, Señorita*. I have come to tell you that soon it will be time for dinner. Would you like me to bring something to you here in your room?'

Megan hesitated. 'Did . . . did *Señor* Porter say I was to dine here?'

Maria shook her head and smiled. 'Oh, no, *Señorita*. He said I was to bring you a tray if you wished . . . if your ankle was hurting you too much. But if you would prefer to join him in the dining-room . . .'

'I would, thank you.' Glancing down at her soiled jeans and shirt, Megan smiled slightly. 'I just hope this is an informal meal,' she said.

The housekeeper smiled and winked. 'I have thought of that,' she said mysteriously. 'When I saw the *Señorita* carried only the packback . . .'

'Backpack,' Megan laughed.

'*Sí*, the backpack. When I saw it, I thought perhaps you might wish to make use of these things.' She stepped back into the hallway and lifted something from a box behind her. Smiling broadly, she held out a long, colourful Mexican skirt, an embroidered white linen blouse, and a pair of leather sandals. 'They will become you well, *Señorita*.'

'But whose are they?'

The woman shrugged and dismissed the question with a wave of her hand. 'They are mine, *Señorita*. There will be drinks on the terrace when you are ready.'

Glancing at the housekeeper, who was considerably shorter and heavier than she was, Megan fought back the desire to burst into laughter. Instead, she nodded her head and smiled.

'Thank you, Maria,' she said gravely. '*Gracias*. You are very kind.'

She started to grin as soon as the door had closed. What a kind thing to do, she told herself. But what a sight she'd make in these lovely things, which would surely be at least three sizes too large for her. Still, it had been a lovely, touching gesture, and she wouldn't hurt the housekeeper's feelings, even if Cam laughed when he saw her . . .

Megan peeled off her clothing, washed, and slipped the soft cotton blouse over her head. It was heavy with embroidered flowers and leaves intricately woven together, and to her surprise, it fitted her body as if made to order. The skirt, a softly draped series of brightly coloured vertical stripes, fitted the same way. Only the sandals were slightly too large, although the extra room was a comfort to her injured foot. She turned to the mirror and stared at herself, delighted by the transformation. How pretty a younger, slimmer Maria must have looked in this outfit. Carefully, she brushed her hair until it fell about her shoulders with gleaming artistry. Cam had never seen her looking this feminine, she thought suddenly, pulling the low-cut blouse down off her shoulders slightly. Would he like the way she looked? Or was he too annoyed at her unwanted presence to react to the change in her appearance? A blush rose to her cheeks and she pulled the blouse back on her shoulders. What did it matter? He was the subject of her next feature, and nothing more than that.

The terrace was deserted, empty except for a cart on which stood glasses and a chilling bottle of wine. Megan walked to the low stone wall and leaned against it, gazing enraptured at the setting sun hanging over the mountain like a burning orange jewel. The evening air was cool and perfumed with a spicy, floral scent, reminiscent of cinammon and jasmine. She shivered and glanced down at herself, wondering whether or not to spoil the beautiful skirt and blouse by adding either her denim jacket or wool sweater to what she was wearing. Perhaps Maria would lend her a shawl . . .

'Where did you get those things?'

Startled, she gasped and spun around. Cam was standing in the doorway to the terrace, an unpleasant scowl on his face.

'From Maria,' Megan said quickly. 'She offered them to me . . . Is there something wrong?'

'From Maria,' he repeated, staring at her intently.

Megan swallowed and nodded her head nervously. 'Yes, that's right. She said they were hers, that I could wear them . . . Look, I'll go in and change, if you don't like the way I look. I thought . . . well, my jeans are pretty soiled . . . and then Maria . . .' She bit back the rest of her hurried explanation, angry at herself for feeling so defensive. 'I've got another pair of jeans in my backpack. They're not much better than the ones I've been wearing, but at least they're clean. I'll only be a minute . . .'

She started to hurry past him and he reached out and grasped her shoulder.

'Never mind,' he growled. 'Wear those things this evening.'

'But . . .'

'I said wear them,' he repeated. 'You look . . . you look fine,' he added more softly. 'I'm sorry if I sounded . . .' His words trailed off and she glanced up at him. 'I was just surprised to see you this way, that's all. And

Maria was right . . . you can't wear those jeans forever.' His hand dropped from her shoulder and he walked across the terrace. 'Would you care for some wine?'

Megan nodded. Although his touch on her shoulder had been light, she could still feel the warmth of his fingers on her skin. She watched as he uncorked the chilled bottle and poured a pale golden liquid into fluted glasses.

'Thank you,' she murmured, taking the glass he held out to her. Her voice sounded faint and uncertain, and he looked at her questioningly.

'How's the ankle? Has it swollen at all?'

She shook her head and sipped at the wine. It had a dry, pleasant taste and a fragrance that seemed to match the scent of flowers on the evening air.

'It's fine, Cam. Please, don't worry about it.'

The silence lengthened between them. Finally, Megan cleared her throat and spoke again.

'What did you do about the dead colt? You said you or your foreman would go up to the meadow and wait for the puma . . .'

'There's no point,' he said. 'Andres rode up this afternoon. The vultures just about finished off the remains. I just hope that's the end of it. Something must have interrupted that puma at his meal—they don't usually run off and leave a kill that way. If he's still hungry, and if he's learned that colts make easy targets, I'm afraid he'll be back.'

Megan nodded in agreement. 'Yes, I know. We had that same problem once with a pair of coyotes that discovered how easy it was to dine on some geese my mother was raising. My Dad finally frightened them off but it took days.'

Cam shook his head and smiled. 'Frightened them

off? The only way to get rid of that kind of killer is with a rifle.'

'Sometimes that's all that works,' she agreed. 'But it's worth trying another way first. After all, the coyotes wanted to eat the geese . . . and so did we. That doesn't make them killers any more than we are, does it?'

'You have an interesting way of looking at it,' he said, his smile broadening. 'And you have a point there. But I'm surprised that a rancher's daughter should see it like that.'

Megan laughed and shrugged her shoulders. 'Ah, you forget. My mother is a biology teacher . . . That gave me a slightly different outlook on predators.'

He re-filled their glasses and sipped at his wine thoughtfully. 'Yes, I suppose it would. Is that why you became interested in wildlife biology? Because of her?'

Again, the unexplained twinge of guilt assailed her and she turned away from him and looked out across the clearing towards the mountains.

'I guess so. I seemed to just drift into it when I got to college,' she said, telling him the truth but, of course, not mentioning that she'd changed her mind after taking a journalism course taught by her ex-husband. 'And what about you? How did you get interested in ranching?'

She heard his footsteps behind her and then she felt the press of his arm against hers as he leaned against the wall beside her.

'I did a film set in Wyoming ten years ago,' he said slowly. 'That started it.'

His arm was still touching hers lightly, and she turned and leaned her back against the wall, moving away a little as she did.

'Just making a film got you involved in all this?'

He laughed quietly and shook his head. 'Sounds

simple, doesn't it? But I spent months researching that part . . . I spoke to ranchers and cowboys, I learned to rope and brand . . . I even lived in a line shack up in the hills outside the ranch we were using as a set. About a year later, I was on location in Durango, shooting a film. This place was for sale, and I realised that I loved this life, that it was something I could be happy at. It took a lot of work to make this ranch what it is . . .' He broke off and drained the last of the wine from his glass. 'Sorry,' he murmured. 'I didn't mean to make a speech.'

'Don't apologise,' Megan said quickly. 'That's fascinating. I've heard about method acting, but I never knew it took so much effort. Do you research all your parts in such depth?'

Cam smiled and shrugged his shoulders. 'Almost all of them. After all, acting is just a way of assuming another identity, isn't it? Well, I can't do that unless I understand the role I'm taking on. So I prepare myself by doing whatever I can to immerse myself in the character I'm going to play.'

'Don't tell me,' Megan laughed, glancing at him. 'I once saw you in a film about gangsters . . .'

'No, I didn't kill anybody to get ready for that one,' he said, chuckling. 'But I did arrange to meet some pretty tough old guys who'd been mob members of the '20s and '30s. What about you? I mean, when you finish this study of yours, what happens next? Will you stay in fieldwork, or do you want to teach at some university?'

She turned away and bit her lip. 'I haven't decided,' she said quickly. 'Anyway, whatever I do, it won't be as exciting as the life you lead.'

Cam grinned and took her empty glass from her. 'Exciting?' he repeated. 'What's exciting about what I do? Oh, I don't mean the acting . . . I love the feeling of adding my own touch to a character, finding ways to make a paper creation come alive. But when I'm working, when I have to be away from here, I spend most of my time dodging people who want to pry and poke at me, who think I'm fair game for the worst sort of gossip. That's part of the reason this place means so much to me, I guess. The only thing that's important here is how well I do my work, not how I look, or who I'm seen with, or . . .' He laughed and set his glass down on the wall. 'Forgive me, Megan. That's the second speech I've made tonight. Believe me, I don't usually talk about myself this much. Look, I promise to shut up while we're having dinner.'

He took her arm and she caught her breath. There it was again. That same feeling of spinning off into space . . . Admit it, Megan, she thought in confusion as he led her into the house, admit it, at least to yourself. You're in trouble. Cam Porter is turning out to be a nice guy, a really nice man. And you're going to stab him in the back, old girl. He does everything he can to stay out of the spotlight when he's not making a film, and you're going to shine that light into the one corner of his life he's managed to protect. You're going to spoil the life he's made for himself here, the life he loves . . .

She glanced up at him as they entered the panelled and beamed dining-room. She had discarded the possibility that his wife was not dead but disfigured almost as soon as Marian had offered it. There would have been doctors and plastic surgeons involved if that had been true; you could hide some things from a curious press, but not when hospitals and lots of people were involved. And he wouldn't have given her a free run of the house if someone were hidden away inside it. Could he feel somehow responsible for his wife's death? That seemed more likely; now that she'd spent time with him, she knew there was a compassionate side to Cam Porter, a caring side . . . but she couldn't imagine he could have driven a woman to suicide. He was too kind, too decent . . . Or was he? Again, Megan looked at his face. He was an actor, after all. It would be easy for him to play at being Mr Nice Guy. He could, in fact, play any role he chose with her. But why would he bother? Surely, not to impress a stranded stranger . . .

Halfway into the room, Cam stopped so abruptly that Megan stumbled against him. 'Maria!' he called, his voice tense with something close to anger. 'Maria, come in here, please.'

The housekeeper pushed open a swinging door at the far end of the room and hurried towards them. '*Sí, Señor?*'

It was impossible for Megan to keep up with Cam's rapid Spanish. He pointed to the table, set with flowers and candles, and Maria nodded and smiled. Her response was as rapid as his, and finally the irritated look faded from his face and he sighed. 'All right, Maria,' he said, glancing at Megan, 'have it your way.'

'Is something wrong?' Megan asked hesitantly. 'Everything looks perfect.'

Cam drew her chair from the table and helped her into it. 'That's just it,' he admitted. 'Everything is. I don't remember the last time I ate by candlelight, unless it was the time the generator blew. And these flowers, Maria must have spent half the afternoon picking and arranging them. It's all for you, Megan. She decided all this was necessary on your behalf.'

'I see,' Megan answered uncomfortably. 'I'm sorry, Cam. I didn't mean to create a problem for her. I can't imagine why she went to all this trouble.'

'I can,' he said quietly. 'She says that a beautiful woman deserves a beautiful setting. And I can't argue with such perfect logic.'

With great effort, Megan forced herself to look away from him. It could all fall into place, if she let it. A man, a woman, a magnificent, romantic setting . . . what better way to improve her chances of learning even more about Cam Porter? If only he'd stop being so . . . so damned nice, she thought furiously. Where was the ice-man Marian had described? For that matter, where was the arrogant man who'd run her off the road only yesterday?

'You're not at all the way I thought you'd be,' she said carefully, arranging her napkin in her lap.

'I thought we settled that this morning. I told you that polo or whatever it is the fan magazines have me doing wasn't my style.'

Megan smiled and shook her head. 'Not that. I meant that yesterday . . . well, if anyone had told me that the guy who made me crash my car, the guy who acted as if I was his personal public enemy, would be saying nice things to me tonight, I'd have accused him of being crazy.'

Cam grinned and served her a bowl of chilled soup. 'This is gazpacho,' he said. 'Have you ever eaten it? It's made of all sorts of fresh vegetables Maria puts together, and it's terrific.'

'Is that your answer? Changing the subject, I mean.'

He shook his head and sighed. 'Okay, I guess I owe you an explanation. You see, I've been careful about Las Montanas en Cielo. No one in the outside world knows about it. Not that they haven't tried; there are some pretty persistent reporters around, and a couple of times they've tailed me from Durango. I thought . . .'

'You thought I was a reporter. Then what you're saying is that if I were, I'd be fair game for a car crash. Don't you think that's a rough way to play?'

He put down his spoon and his face whitened. 'There was never any danger of your crashing, Megan. All I did was stop your car on a safe stretch of road.' He took a deep breath and nodded his head. 'All right, I guess when you put it like that, it seems kind of rough. But if you walked in my shoes for a while, if people thought it was open season on your personal life, you might understand.'

She swallowed a mouthful of gazpacho and smiled appreciatively. 'You were right—this is delicious. Maybe you're right about reporters, too. But they have a job to do, Cam. And they pass information along to your fans, to the people who paid the money so that you could buy this ranch. Did you ever think of it that way?'

He put down his fork and stared at her. She held her breath, wondering if she'd said too much, and then he shook his head and poured more wine into their glasses.

'That's an over-simplification, Megan. What I owe my fans—I hate that word, by the way—what I owe them is the best performance I can give each time I make a film. I'm an actor,' he said, his voice stressing the word. 'I've chosen to make my living by communicating human feelings, human attitudes. That doesn't give anybody the right to pry at me, to distort whatever I do and whomever I do it with.'

'Is there a "whomever"?' she asked brightly. 'I haven't seen a sign of anybody else here.'

'You're leaving out Maria, Andres, and at least six vaqueros who help me run this place,' he laughed. 'And finish your soup. Maria will never forgive you if you don't.'

She smiled and shook her head. 'I'm leaving room for whatever it is that's hidden in that other serving dish. And you haven't answered my question.'

'I have,' he said solemnly. 'I've just named all the people who share Las Montanas en Cielo with me.'

'No one else?' Megan persisted, and the pleasant look faded from his face.

'Why are you so interested?' he asked gruffly.

'I guess I remember how it was for my folks, living on their ranch in Arizona,' she answered quickly, afraid she'd gone too far. 'They loved their land, the way you love yours. But the nearest town was thirty miles away, and the closest neighbour was only ten miles less than that. You're even more alone out here. I guess I just assumed you'd want someone to share all this with. I mean, my folks had each other, and I thought . . .' Her words trailed off lamely into the silence.

'You have a way of getting right to the heart of things, haven't you? Your parents were lucky people, Megan. I'm afraid I haven't been quite that fortunate.' She looked up, surprised at the emptiness in his voice, and he smiled at her. 'Although I wouldn't let Maria hear me say that,' he added. 'She's taken on the role of adoptive *mamacita*, I think. And she'll be in here in a couple of minutes, angry as hell if we don't get to the next course.' He uncovered the remaining platter and a delicate hint of garlic wafted up from it. 'Well, she may be an incurable romantic when it comes to table settings,' he said, with a chuckle, 'but it doesn't seem to extend to her cooking. This is one of her specialities. *Carne a la Tampiquena*—steak with tortillas, guacamole, refried beans . . .'

'Are we really supposed to eat all that?' Megan groaned. 'It looks wonderful, but there's enough to serve us, all your vaqueros, and half the town of Durango!'

Cam grinned as he filled Megan's plate. 'She already told me she thinks you're too skinny, even though I insisted you were perfect just the way you are. And I'd better warn you, Megan. She's probably out in the kitchen, fussing with dessert.'

In fact, the fresh mango and cheese the housekeeper brought to the dining-room half an hour later remained untouched. Megan was sure she'd never be able to fit into her old jeans again, and when Cam suggested they have their coffee on the terrace, she agreed eagerly, hoping the cool night air would dispel the sleepy, languid feeling that dinner had brought on.

The night sky was a dark, velvet canopy overhead, ablaze with the remote silver fire of the stars. An almost palpable silence seemed to surround them as they stepped outside, a silence broken only by the faint sighing of the pines as they dipped their branches in the caress of a gentle breeze.

'Oh, Cam,' Megan whispered finally, 'I've never seen anything more beautiful.'

'Yes,' he murmured, 'it's an incredible sight, isn't it? There's a clearing just a little way from the terrace; if you stand in it and look up, the stars make you feel as if you're floating somewhere out in space. Here, I'll show you . . .' He cupped her elbow in his hand and she shivered involuntarily. 'Are you cool, Megan? I should have realised you wouldn't be warm enough without a jacket. We can go back inside, if you like.'

'No,' she said quickly, 'no, I'm fine. It's a little cool, but I'd like to stay out here for just a bit.'

He slipped out of his jacket and put it around her shoulders. 'Is that better?' he asked, and she nodded her head, painfully aware of the fact that his arm remained lightly draped around her. 'I should have asked Maria to get you a scarf to go with what you're wearing. I'll remind her later.'

'It was kind enough of her to have lent me this, Cam.'

His arm tightened slightly as he led her down the steps

and off the terrace. 'It was more than kind,' he murmured, 'it was inspired. You look lovely.'

'Thank you,' she whispered, grateful for the darkness
that hid the blush she felt spreading over her cheeks.
'When I return these things to her, I'll tell her you
approved.'

They were moving away from the house, and the
silken blackness of the Mexican night seemed to be
closing in around them. Megan could feel the dampness
of the grass through the open straps of the sandals.

'Don't return them,' Cam said quickly. 'Keep them.
Those things look as if they were made for you.'

Megan shook her head. 'I couldn't . . . Maria . . .'

His voice was so low she had to strain to hear what he
said. 'The clothes aren't hers, Megan. They belonged to
. . . to someone else. I thought Maria had disposed of all
those things. Now, I'm glad she didn't.'

'Someone else?' Megan repeated.'

'I was married,' he said flatly. 'My wife died years ago.
The clothing you're wearing belonged to her.'

'You mean . . . I wouldn't have accepted it if I'd
known,' she said quickly. 'I'm sorry, Cam. I
thought . . .'

He turned towards her and shook his head, his face
barely visible in the moonlight filtering through the pines
that surrounded the house.

'There's nothing to be sorry for, Megan. My wife
never wore those things; there were boxes of dresses and
skirts—all sorts of stuff—that came from Acapulco and
Puerto Vallarta after her death. She'd been on a shopping spree just before the accident.' He made a sound
that might have been a laugh. 'Actually, she was always
on a shopping spree. That's one of the things she hated
about the ranch. It's kind of difficult to use a charge card
here.'

'What kind of accident was it?'

His eyes narrowed in painful remembrance. 'She ran her car off a cliff up around Copper Canyon,' he said finally, his voice flat and emotionless. 'She must have been doing at least a hundred miles an hour—she tore straight through a barricade. When I went up there a couple of days later . . .'

'Why?' Megan asked quickly. 'Why did you go there?'

'I wanted to see where it happened,' he said quietly. 'I was on location in Canada when she . . . when it happened. It was horrible, Megan. It must have been a thousand feet to the bottom of that gorge. It took days to get . . . everything out.'

Instinctively, she reached out and touched his shoulder. There was a pained anguish in his eyes and voice that made her want to take him into her arms and comfort him.

'My God,' she whispered, 'how awful. To get news like that . . .'

His hand closed over hers and he nodded his head. 'Yes, but I'd been expecting something for years. Sally was a sweet girl, but she was always troubled. Even before we got married.'

'Don't talk about it, Cam,' Megan murmured, not caring that he was about to tell her the story she'd come here for. 'It's over. It can only hurt to talk about it.'

He shook his head and a look that seemed to come from the furthest corners of his soul filled his eyes. 'The marriage had ended long before she died. It's the way she died . . .' His words trailed off and when he spoke again, his voice was filled with anger and bitterness. 'Almost from the start, I knew it was a mistake. We wanted different things from the marriage, we had different needs . . . But she was my wife, and I tried to make a go of it. She was so vulnerable . . . She knew the marriage wasn't working, and I guess she started believing all the garbage she read in the columns.' His hand tightened painfully around Megan's and she winced. 'All of it,' he muttered. 'I tried telling her most of what she read was untrue, but it was useless. I even called a couple of reporters who'd printed things . . . distorted things, things that made a simple business lunch with a woman sound like the affair of the decade, but I got nowhere.'

'And Sally . . . your wife . . . she believed what she read about you?'

He laughed bitterly. 'Believed them? She died for them, Megan. There's only so much doctors and pills can do for that kind of depression.' He shook his head. 'Maybe it would have been kinder to have divorced her when the marriage first began to go down the tubes,' he said quietly. 'I sometimes wonder . . .'

Megan squeezed his hand between both of hers and shook her head.

'Don't,' she said quickly. 'You did the best you could, Cam. I know how that is . . . staying with somebody because you feel it's the right thing to do. If she was troubled, leaving her wouldn't have prevented her death.'

'It would have protected her from the acid that dripped out of the pens of those damned reporters,' he growled. 'They pushed her over the edge, Megan. They . . .' He drew in his breath and closed his eyes. 'God, what am I doing?' he murmured. 'I can't believe I said all this . . . I've never talked about Sally's death to anyone, until tonight.'

'I'm glad you told me, Cam. Sometimes it helps to share a burden with someone else.'

He smiled and moved closer to her. 'Maybe you're right, Megan. I never thought I'd want to talk about it . . . but it's so easy to talk to you. I feel as if we've known each other for years. Maybe it has something to do with the way we met—on a road in Mexico, where I wasn't Cam Porter but just a man helping a lovely woman . . . although I was really the one who got you into that mess in the first place.'

A wave of guilt washed over Megan and she drew her hand from his. 'I got myself into it,' she said quickly, turning away from him. 'Believe me, Cam, it was my fault, not yours.'

'Well, then, I'm grateful to you. Without that run-in yesterday, we wouldn't have met.'

'It's getting late,' she whispered, fighting against the desire to turn and run into the black night and out of his life this very moment. 'Thank you for a lovely evening, Cam.'

He smiled and drew the edges of his jacket together under her chin. 'It's I who should thank you,' he said softly.

'For what?' she managed to whisper as his fingers brushed against her neck. 'For being an uninvited guest? For keeping you from doing what you'd planned on doing up in that meadow today? For . . .'

His hands moved from the jacket and cupped her face. 'For all of that,' he said softly, 'and for so much more.'

Slowly, she raised her face to his, powerless to prevent what she knew would happen, wanting the moment as much as she feared it, and his mouth met hers. His lips were warm and tender, demanding nothing but promising everything. She tried to think, to remind herself that this was Cameron Porter, her victim, her quarry, but it was useless. Her eyes closed and she swayed towards him, as once again a drowning sense of vertigo swept over her, but there was a sweetness to it this time, a peacefulness that made her sigh even as he kissed her. Cam's hands moved to her shoulders, bringing her closer against him, and she came willingly, effortlessly, as her arms wound around his neck. She felt his mouth moving on hers, promising more, asking all, and she sighed as her lips parted gently under the heat of his. The jacket slipped from her shoulders and fell, unheeded, to the grass at their feet. Cam's lips moved gently from hers, and she could feel the feathery warmth of his breath against her cheek, her ear, her neck until finally he was kissing the soft hollow at the base of her throat.

'Megan,' he whispered huskily against her skin, 'Megan . . .'

There was a rustle in the nearby trees and an animal cried out softly. In a rush of reality, Megan's eyes flew open. 'Don't,' she murmured. 'Cam, please . . . we can't . . .' She put her hands against his chest and stepped back from his encircling arms. 'You don't understand . . .'

'You're right,' he said quickly, drawing her against him again. 'I don't understand. I only know this is right, Megan. Ever since this morning, when I thought you'd been hurt, when I held you in my arms . . . I tried to tell you then. I said it was impossible for you to stay here.'

She drew in her breath. 'Is that what you meant?' she whispered, her voice breaking. 'I thought . . .' She closed her eyes and turned her head away from his, afraid he would see the anguish and self-disgust she knew must be etched on her face. 'Cam, I can't. Please, let me go. Let me go back into the house now. This isn't what I wanted, what I expected . . .'

The silence of the vast night fell over them. An eternity measured in heartbeats seemed to pass before his arms fell to his sides and he stepped back from her.

'Of course, it isn't,' he said stiffly. 'Forgive me, please, Megan. I'm not myself tonight. I won't bother you again.'

'Don't say it like that,' she cried. 'I didn't mean it the way it sounded. If you only understood . . . you've been so kind, so nice . . . and you've been hurt so badly . . .'

She heard his sudden, sharp intake of breath. 'Dear God, Megan, that's not what this was all about. I didn't tell you about Sally so you would . . .'

'That isn't what I meant, Cam. Please . . .'

He bent and picked up the jacket, carefully draping it around her shoulders without once touching her.

'It was my mistake, Megan. I thought you felt something . . .' He shook his head and laughed softly. 'I guess that's what I wanted to think,' he said quietly. 'I apologise if I embarrassed you. Now, go on into the house and don't worry; I'm certain I'll be able to get through to the village in the morning. And, if I can't, I'll drive you back to Durango myself.'

She took a hesitant step forward, torn by the emotions raging through her, wanting to tell him the truth, wanting to tell him that being in his arms moments before made everything she'd come here to do seem cheap and meaningless. And then what? she thought suddenly. What would he think, what would he say, once he knew she had lied to him, tricked him, deceived him every step of the way?

He reached out and touched her cheek gently. 'Go back inside the house, Megan,' he murmured. 'I'm sorry.'

He turned abruptly and walked away from her, and his last, whispered comment seemed to be an echoing mockery of her own despair.

CHAPTER SIX

MEGAN's bedroom was wrapped in the same velvet darkness that covered the silent Sierra Madre Mountains. The luminous face of her wristwatch was like the light of a tiny star glowing on her wrist, a pale green beacon marking the hour of two in the morning, a reminder that the seconds and minutes were dragging towards dawn with infinite slowness. She yearned for the comfort of sleep, for at least a temporary end to the whirling confusion of her thoughts, but sleep was an elusive ally. Each time she closed her eyes, she saw Cam's face as it had looked when he kissed her. It was as if those moments spent with him in the clearing had been etched into her memory and would torment her forever.

She rolled over in the bed and drew the blanket up to her chin. What on earth had happened to her? There had been men in her life in the five years since her divorce from Jeff, several of them, in fact. There was always someone pleasant and interesting to have dinner with, to see a play with, to share a day or an evening. And she'd kissed some of them . . . but never the way she'd kissed Cam. That feeling, that desire to melt into a man's arms, to become lost in his embrace, was something only faintly remembered from the beginning of her relationship with Jeff.

Closing her eyes, Megan burrowed into the warmth and security of the blanket. She had come here to do a story, not to become involved with her subject, and keeping an objective distance was the first rule of her profession. It was the first rule of her personal life as well, she admitted, smoothing the rumpled pillowcase under her cheek. Becoming involved in a relationship just hadn't seemed worth the energy it would divert from her career, or the pain it might cause. At least, living with Jeff had taught her that much. There'd been opportunities, of course, but never the desire to break the rule . . . until now.

With an irritated shake of her head, Megan sat up in bed and propped the pillow behind her. It would be daylight in a few hours, and Cam had promised to get her back to Durango, one way or another. Well, she thought, clasping her hands around her knees, the sooner she left Las Montanas en Cielo, the better. There might be a story here, but it was not a story she intended to tell. Once, years before in a journalism class, she'd argued with a fellow student about a journalist's obligation to report a story.

'Sometimes,' he'd insisted, 'you have to make a moral judgment and walk away from a story.'

'Never,' she'd sworn, with an idealistic self-righteousness that embarrassed her as she remembered it. 'I'll never do that.'

She sighed and switched on the bedside light. How could she have known that her vow had been made only to be broken on a quiet, starry night in Mexico? If only there were a way to leave the ranch without seeing Cam again, a way to get to Durango, fly out on the very first plane, and get back to the comfort and safety of New York and her typewriter. The article on Dr Dan and Inner Success was still waiting to be written—there hadn't been time to do it.

'The Cam Porter piece can't wait,' Marian had said emphatically. 'Dr Dan can.'

She could bury herself in her work, get that article

about Dr Dan on Marian's desk in a couple of days . . .

Megan groaned and hung her head. What on earth was she going to say to Marian? That she had no story because she hadn't seen Cam's plane land in Durango? Impossible . . . if that were the case, she'd have phoned New York right away. That she'd found Cam, but there was no story? No disfigured wife, no guilty complicity on Cam's part . . .? Her breath hissed between her teeth and she shook her head. Of course there was a story, Marian would say. She'd found Cam's hideaway, hadn't she? He'd told her something about his marriage and his wife's death . . . she even had photos of him and the ranch . . .

She tossed aside the covers and got up from the rumpled bed, ignoring the sting of the chilled air against her bare skin.

'There's got to be something you can tell her,' she muttered as she paced back and forth. 'There must be . . .' Her footsteps slowed and a slow, pleased smile touched her lips. Of course there was. She'd tell Marian she'd followed Cam south from Durango, not north, that she lost him somewhere near Chiahuahua and spent the next couple of days trying to find him. It was not only plausible, it was perfect misdirection. If Marian ever mentioned it to anyone, or sent another reporter on the same assignment, they'd drive hundreds of miles in the wrong direction. Cam would be safe. And he'd never have to know what she'd almost done to him.

'Megan?' She spun around and stared at the door. 'Megan? Are you awake?'

It was Cam's voice, low pitched but clear in the silence of the night, and there was an undercurrent of distress in it. Megan grabbed the blanket from the bed and wrapped it around herself.

To Susan Welland
**Mills & Boon
Reader Service
FREEPOST
P.O. Box 236
CROYDON
Surrey CR9 9EL.**

FREE BOOKS CERTIFICATE

Dear Susan,

Your special introductory offer of 12 free books is too good to miss. I understand they are mine to keep with the free necklace. Please also reserve a Reader Service Subscription for me. If I decide to subscribe, I shall, from the beginning of the month following my free parcel of books, receive 12 new books each month for £14.40, post and packing free. If I decide not to subscribe, I shall write to you within 10 days. The free books will be mine to keep, in any case. I understand that I may cancel my subscription at any time simply by writing to you. I am over 18 years of age.

10A6TA

Signature _____

Name _____
(BLOCK CAPITALS PLEASE)
Address _____

Postcode _____

'What is it?' she whispered, opening the door a crack. 'Is something wrong?'

He was still dressed as he had been during dinner, she noticed, although a shock of hair and fallen across his forehead and there was a dark smear on the front of his jacket.

'I'm sorry if I startled you,' he said apologetically, 'but . . . look, I know this sounds crazy, but you said you grew up on a ranch. I was wondering . . . did you ever help deliver a foal?'

'Deliver a . . .? Well, I didn't actually do anything, but I watched often enough when my mother helped my father. But I don't understand . . .'

'One of my mares is in labour,' he said quickly. 'She came into season early, and by the time we realised what had happened, she'd already been bred. I figured she was due to drop her foal in about two weeks, but when I went to the stable after dinner, I found her in labour. I waited with her, but it's been hours . . .' He paused and ran his hand through his hair. 'Am I making any sense? I feel as if I'm telling this so rapidly that none of it's coming out straight.

'Is she in trouble?' Megan asked quickly, opening the door fully. 'Are you going to lose her or the colt?'

'It may come to that, if I don't do something fast. Miguel and the other men went up to that blind canyon we were at this morning. I was worried that the puma might come back . . .' A fleeting smile crossed his face. 'Miguel wanted to set out some poisoned bait, but I told him to try another way first. I need your help, Megan. I want to examine the mare, but she's terrified. Will you come with me?

Her response was swift and unhesitating. 'Of course. Just give me a minute to get ready.'

Cam was waiting for her when she came running into

the hay-scented, dimly lit stable. He'd tossed his jacket aside and rolled up the sleeves of his shirt, and he took her arm and hurried her to a straw-bestrewn padded birthing-stall set apart from the others.

'The mare is young,' he explained in a worried whisper. 'She's never dropped a foal before, and she's getting weaker by the minute. I'm afraid we may lose her, if it takes much longer.'

'We won't lose her,' Megan said firmly. 'She'll be fine.'

But her easy assurances faded as soon as she saw the animal. The horse's chestnut flanks were damp and flecked with foam, and the heavy rasp of her breathing was harsh and laboured.

'Easy girl,' Megan whispered, stroking the finely chiselled nose of the distraught animal. 'You're going to be okay in just a little while.' The mare whinnied softly and tossed her head, nuzzling her damp muzzle into Megan's shoulder. 'Do you have any idea what's wrong, Cam?'

He nodded grimly and drew on long rubber gloves. 'I have a feeling the foal is turned wrong,' he said quietly. 'I'm going to feel for it right now . . . can you steady her, Megan? Hold her head still and reassure her somehow . . .'

Megan nodded and grasped the mare's ears gently, pulling the frightened animal's head down until it rested against hers, all the while whispering soft words of reassurance against the damp, coarse mane.

'You were right, Cam,' she said. 'She's been in labour longer than she should. If she doesn't drop the foal soon, she's going to be frantic. It'll be impossible to hold her then.'

As if to prove the point, the horse pulled its head free of Megan's restraining hands and shied to the side of the stall. Cam moved quickly, leaning against her flanks to steady her as Megan stumbled clear of the heavy, distended body.

'Megan? Are you hurt? Megan . . . .'

'I'm fine,' she answered breathlessly. 'She just got away from me for a second.'

'There's a bridle hanging just outside there, on the wall by the door,' he grunted, using all his weight to keep the mare from lumbering back across the enclosed space. 'Can you get it on her?'

Megan nodded. She snatched up the bridle and approached the trembling mare, speaking soft, soothing words as she reached for the arching neck.

'Okay,' she said finally, 'I've got it on her. Go on and feel for the foal, Cam—I can hold her. What's her name?'

He chuckled softly. 'Bonita,' he said. 'I'm sorry that there wasn't time for a more formal introduction. Okay . . . if you can just hang on to her for another minute or two, Megan . . . I've almost finished . . .'

'Easy, girl,' Megan whispered, pressing her head close to the mare's neck. 'It's going to be okay, Bonita. We're going to help you.'

'That's what I thought,' Cam muttered. 'The foal is breech.'

The mare pulled hard against the bridle, but Megan hung on with grim determination, whispering encouragement as she did.

'Everything's going to be fine,' she said quietly. 'It is, isn't it, Cam? Can you feel the foal's legs?'

His voice was tense with concentration. 'Yes, thank God. They're in the passage . . . all he needs is a little help.'

He peeled off the gloves and went to the back of the stable, returning quickly with a length of rope. As he pulled the gloves on again, he glanced at Megan and nodded encouragingly.

'Okay, this should do it. I'm going to secure his legs and help pull him free. How are you doing, Megan? Are you all right?'

She nodded and returned his smile. 'Yes, I'm fine. Just be sure you don't pull until Bonnie pushes.'

He flashed her a quick grin. 'Bonnie, hmm? I never knew she preferred to be called Bonnie.'

'We women tell each other lots of things you men will never know. And she just said she's just about ready to send that little guy out into the world . . .'

'And she's right,' he answered, grunting with the strain he was putting on the rope. 'Hang on, Megan. Okay, Bonnie . . . do your best!'

The mare snorted as another contraction racked her body. Megan hung on to the bridle as Cam called out words of encouragement.

'Okay, he's moving . . . his hooves are free . . . that's it, Bonnie. Just a little more . . .'

The horse whinnied softly and tossed her head.

'You're doing fine, girl,' Megan whispered. 'It's almost over.' She raised her shoulder and wiped her forehead against her sleeve. Suddenly, she felt the mare tensing and she planted her feet more firmly and tightened her grip on the bridle. 'She's going to push again, Cam. I can feel it coming.'

'That was a good one, Bonnie,' Cam grunted. 'A few more like that and you'll have your girlish figure back.'

'What a thing to say!' Megan laughed as the mare bumped her nose into the crook of her neck. 'Bonnie says to tell you that's the last thing on her mind right now.'

'I'm just appealing to her feminine vanity . . . trying to give her a reason to work harder. Come on, Bonnie.

One more good shove and your baby will drop into my hands.' He peered at Megan around the side of the horse. 'How are you doing? Your arms must ache . . .'

'Not a bit,' she lied, gritting her teeth. 'You just worry about Mama and forget about me.'

He grinned and touched his finger to his damp hair. 'Yes ma'am,' he said. 'That's what I'll do. I . . .'

The mare's muscles contracted and she made a sound that was more a human moan than a whinny.

'Hang on, Megan,' Cam yelled. 'I think this is it. Come on, Bonnie. You can do it, girl.'

He grunted and pulled on the rope as Megan twisted her fingers into the sweat-soaked bridle, and suddenly it was over. As Cam and Megan both cheered, the newborn foal slipped easily to the clean, hay-strewn floor. Cam bent quickly and then he looked up and grinned.

'Well, I was wrong about one thing. It's not a colt, it's a filly. And a beautiful one, Bonita. You did a terrific job, old girl.' He patted the mare's flank and motioned to Megan. 'Why don't you come on back here and say hello to this little lady?'

Megan stroked the mare's neck and pressed a kiss against her nose. 'Good girl,' she whispered. 'I'll be right back; I just want to get a look at your baby.' She moved back towards Cam and dropped to her knees beside him. 'Oh, just look at her,' she murmured with delight. 'She's adorable.'

Cam had just finished rubbing down the damply glistening foal with a rough towel. As Megan watched, the youngster raised its head and shook it. With comical solemnity, it got to its feet, wobbling a bit as its long legs threatened to collapse under it, and Cam gently turned the sturdy little body towards the mare.

'Say hello to your daughter, Bonita,' he said quietly.

Whinnying softly, the mare bent her head and licked

the newborn foal. The little one swayed back and forth
for a few seconds, then turned towards its mother's
flanks and, with unfailing certainy, began to nurse. Cam
smiled at Megan and shook his head.

'Never fails to amaze me,' he said softly. 'I've seen
these guys born dozens of times, but it still strikes me as
some kind of miracle.' He took Megan's hand and
helped her to her feet. 'Just a couple of minutes more,
Megan. I want to rub the mare down and clean up a
bit.'

She watched silently as Cam went about his work.
There were smudges of dirt on his cheek and a rip in the
sleeve of his shirt, but he seemed oblivious to anything
but the horse and her foal, and he paused every now and
then to pet Bonita and whisper a few words to her.
Smiling to herself, Megan took a pitchfork from the wall
and removed the soiled straw from the stall, tossing it
into a refuse bin and then adding clean, fresh bedding
from a pile near the door. After dumping Cam's discarded rubber gloves and rope into a sink along the back
wall of the stable, she returned to the birthing-stall,
wiped her hands on her jeans and looked at Cam as he
knelt beside the foal and ran his hands along its long,
slightly unsteady legs.

'I don't think we'll have to worry about this little one,'
he murmured with satisfaction. 'She may have come into
the world rather reluctantly, but she's in fine shape.'

Megan chuckled as she smoothed the hair back from
her forehead. 'Wouldn't you be reluctant to be born too
soon? She's going to have to wait months for proper
playmates. Just look at that,' she laughed as the foal
nuzzled its mother again. 'What an appetite she has!'

'Hard work will do that to you every time,' he agreed
with a grin. The mare tossed her head and snickered
softly as she tried to shy away from her persistent

offspring. 'I just hope Bonnie plans on co-operating,' Cam added.

'Of course she will, Cam. She's its mother, after all.'

'She gave birth to this baby, Megan,' he said, getting to his feet and stroking the nervous horse. 'That doesn't mean she'll make a good job of raising it. You must have seen mares reject foals on your folks' ranch.'

'Well, yes, once in a while,' she admitted slowly. 'But not often. You just said birth was like a miracle.'

Cam gave Bonita a final, reassuring pat and then walked to the rear of the stable. 'Sure,' he said, washing his hands at the utility sink. 'But that's the easy part.'

'Easy?' Megan laughed as she handed him a rough towel from the rack beside the sink. 'Try telling that to Bonnie.'

'Oh, it's hard work,' he grinned, tossing the towel aside. 'No doubt about that. But it's what comes next that's really tough. Giving life is only the beginning, Megan. Nurturing it is the real test.'

She watched as he rolled down his shirt sleeves and buttoned his cuffs. 'Maybe you're right,' she said finally. 'I always thought of mothering as a kind of instinct animals have.'

'Instinct isn't always enough. Not with animals, and certainly not with people.' He glanced at Megan and frowned. 'What is it? Have I offended your feminine beliefs?'

Megan shook her head and turned away from him. 'No, not at all. I . . . I was just thinking of someone I once knew who wouldn't agree with you.'

'Then he's a fool,' Cam said abruptly. 'Believe me, I could tell him a thing or two that would change his mind.' His face softened as he looked at the mare and foal. 'Well, so far, so good. Bonita—excuse me, Bonnie —seems to have got the hang of things. I think we can leave these two alone for a while and get some rest. You must be exhausted.'

'As a matter of fact, I am,' she admitted, 'even though Bonnie did all the work.'

Cam shook his head. 'Not quite,' he said softly. 'She couldn't have done it without you, and neither could I. Thanks for cleaning up, by the way. You didn't have to.'

Megan smiled and shrugged her shoulders. 'No problem,' she said lightly. 'I've cleaned up worse messes in barns before. Actually, I feel right at home in this kind of setting.'

His eyes swept over her as he moved towards her. 'You look right at home,' he murmured, pausing a few inches away. 'And you look beautiful.'

'I look terrible,' she said quickly, trying to sound light-hearted and casual. 'Unless uncombed hair and dirty clothes are fashionable this year.'

'You're lovely, Megan. I wouldn't change a thing about you . . . not even that smudge of dirt on your face,' he said, smiling at her.

He ran his finger lightly across her cheek. His touch was like a burning brand against her skin, and she trembled involuntarily and drew away from him.

'On second thoughts,' she said nervously, 'I think I'd better wait for breakfast. Just look at the time . . . the sun will be coming up soon.'

'We can watch the sun rise from the terrace,' he said quietly, reaching out and smoothing the hair back from her flushed cheeks. 'I'll make some coffee, and . . .'

'No,' she whispered, moving past him and hurrying to the door. 'No, don't do that, Cam.'

He caught up to her as she headed towards the safety of the house and walked beside her.

'Why are you running away from me, Megan? Is it

because of what happened after dinner? Are you afraid of me?'

'Afraid . . .?' Her voice broke and she shook her head. 'God, no, it's not that.'

'Then why won't you talk to me? Megan . . .' They reached the front door and he grasped her arm and turned her to face him. 'Why won't you look at me?' he demanded.

She could see his face clearly in the first pale hint of dawn as it broke over the mountains. His eyes, as blue and clear as the ocean that kissed the sand on the other side of the Sierra Madres, were filled with a thousand questions she could not answer. With a tremulous smile, she shook her head and caught her lower lip between her teeth.

'It's late,' she said quickly. 'I'm too tired to talk now . . . I have to shower, and get some sleep. We both do.'

His hand moved up her arm and she felt the touch of his fingers against her neck. She closed her eyes, fighting against the desire to turn her face to the palm of his hand and press her lips against his skin.

'Cam,' she whispered, 'please, let me go.'

He ran his hand up the back of her neck, into the thick tangle of chestnut hair that spilled down her back and she moved her head, nestling it into his palm, relaxing under his gentle caress, not really aware of what she was doing until, suddenly, her eyes flew open and she pulled away from him.

'No, please,' she whispered. 'I'm too tired to think, Cam. I can't make sense out of anything.'

'You're right,' he said softly. 'This isn't the right time . . . I'll see you in the morning.'

Wearily, she nodded her head. 'Yes,' she murmured, 'I'll see you then.'

The quiet of the house and the night settled around

them. Cam stepped away from her, but Megan remained standing where she was, uncertain if she had the strength to walk away from him. Finally, she took a deep breath and started down the hall towards her room.

'Megan . . .' Her steps slowed at his whispered call and she turned and looked at him. 'The reason I didn't go to sleep tonight . . . the reason I was up checking on the mare at that hour . . .' He took a step towards her and stopped. 'I kept thinking about what happened this evening,' he murmured, and she flushed and lowered her eyelids. 'I wasn't wrong when I thought you wanted me to kiss you, was I? You felt the same thing I did, Megan. The way you kissed me . . . that wasn't the kiss of a woman who doesn't feel something for a man, was it?'

She could hear the sound of her own heart beating as it raced within her, and although she knew, without question, what her answer should be, she shook her head and found there was no way to live with herself another day and go on lying to him about what she had felt in his arms.

'No,' she answered, the whispered word a sigh, 'no, it wasn't. I tried to tell you . . . I wanted to tell you . . .' She held up her hand as he began to move closer. 'Don't,' she said quickly. 'Cam, you don't understand. What you said about this being impossible . . . about you and me. You were right.'

'Is there another man? Is that the reason? Is there someone waiting for you back in the States?'

'No, no, there's no one. There hasn't been anyone in years . . . Not since my divorce. You don't even know that I was married once,' she said, her words running together in a breathless tangle. 'You don't know anything about me.'

He smiled and shook his head. 'I know everything I

need to know,' he said softly, 'now that you've told me there's no one else.'

'There's more you should know,' Megan said, almost angrily. 'So much more, Cam.'

The warmth of his smile seemed to shorten the distance between them. 'Of course there is,' he murmured. 'I want to know everything about you . . . what books you read, what your favourite colour is, the things you like to do on rainy Sunday afternoons . . . why it is you like to walk in the rain,' he said, and she started to smile. 'You do, don't you?'

She nodded her head. 'How did you know that?' she whispered.

She stood, transfixed, as he walked towards her. 'It was easy,' he whispered. 'I feel as if I've known you all my life.' Gently, he tilted her face up to his, and his lips brushed lightly against hers.

'Cam . . . this is crazy. It can't work . . .'

'Get some rest,' he said softly. 'I'll see you in the morning.'

She felt the touch of his mouth against hers, and then he was gone.

CHAPTER SEVEN

MEGAN awoke abruptly from a disturbed, dream-racked sleep. She had been dreaming of Cam—he'd been holding her in his arms, kissing her, when suddenly thousands of bright lights had been turned on them and she realised they were standing on a huge stage. Cam's face had angered, then saddened, blurring softly before her eyes until it swam out of focus and then reappeared as an enormous, blown up *Sophisticate* magazine cover with her by-line splashed across it. She shuddered as she stumbled out of the twisted bed sheets.

She could hear the muffled calls of the vaqueros as they worked in the corrals near the house. It was late —past ten, according to her watch. On a working ranch such as this, everyone would have been up and busy for hours. Still, she moved slowly, deliberately taking her time as she showered and dressed, glancing out of the window every now and then, until finally she saw Cam and three of his men cut horses out of the herd in a far corral, saddle them, and ride off.

Her eyes felt heavy with weariness and the burden of unshed tears as she began to toss her few belongings into her backpack. She had been planning this moment for hours, delaying it only until she was certain Cam was not nearby. The decision to leave without seeing him again had not been an easy one to reach, but it was the only one she could make. She was none of the things he thought: the kindest names she had called herself after he'd left her just before dawn were liar and impostor. To leave him now was the hardest thing she'd ever done, but it was a thousand times easier than leaving him later. If she stayed, there would be no possible way to tear herself from his arms the next time he kissed her—she knew that as surely as she knew that what she felt for him was far more than physical desire. And then she would want to bare her soul to him, tell him the truth and plead for understanding and forgiveness. But those would not be the things she would see in Cam's eyes, once he knew the truth. Desire and tenderness would turn to hatred and anger at her betrayal. No, she thought adamantly, stuffing her last few belongings into the pack, it was best to get out now, before it was too late to rip free of the tangle of emotions that was snaring her in its silken web.

As it was, when she'd heard his soft tap at her door hours earlier, it had taken all the strength she possessed not to leap from the bed and run to his arms. And an hour later, when he'd come to her door again, she'd been amazed she was able to answer, forcing herself to sound sleepy and distant, calling out that she was tired and needed just a little more rest before breakfast. For a second, she'd held her breath, wondering what would happen to all her resolve to flee if he opened the door and came to her, but after a brief pause, he'd chuckled softly and said she'd earned another hour's sleep. She'd let out her breath only when she heard his footsteps moving off down the hall. Exhaustion had drawn her back into a fitful sleep until only moments ago.

Now, working quickly to stay within the brief, uncertain margin of safety his absence provided, Megan strapped the backpack closed, grabbed up her rolled sleeping-bag, and hurried from the bedroom. At the door to the kitchen she hesitated, forcing what she fervently hoped was a pleasant smile to her lips.

'*Buenos días*, Maria,' she said. 'How are you this morning?'

The housekeeper turned towards her and smiled. 'Ah, *Señorita* Stevens, *buenos días. Señor* Porter will be disappointed; he waited for you until just a few minutes ago. Perhaps he is still outside. I can ask Miguel to go after him.'

'No!' The woman's eyes widened at Megan's sharp cry, and again she forced a smile to her face until she felt as if she were wearing a mask. 'No, don't bother him, please, Maria,' she said more calmly. 'I'll see him when he gets back.'

Maria nodded her head. '*Sí*, he will return for lunch. I am preparing something special. But how foolish I am, *Señorita*,' she said, clucking her tongue and reaching for a pot of coffee on the back burner of the stove. 'I speak of lunch, and you have not yet had breakfast. I kept some bacon warm for you, unless you would prefer some of the *pan dulce* you had yesterday. You can decide while you have your coffee. No?' she asked with a frown when Megan shook her head. 'No breakfast?'

'No coffee,' Megan corrected. 'I haven't the time this morning, Maria.'

'But *Señorita* . . .'

'Maria—I wonder, do you know if *Señor* Porter managed to reach anyone in the village? He was supposed to arrange a ride back to Durango for me today.'

The housekeeper looked puzzled. 'I do not think so, *Señorita*,' she said slowly. 'The *Señor* told me to chill some wine for dinner—the one you liked so much—and to have Miguel start a fire later this afternoon for the *carne asada*—it is like, how you say, a barbecue. He thought you would enjoy it.'

Megan caught her lower lip between her teeth. 'I see,' she murmured. 'Uh . . . what about the telephone lines? Are they still out, or can I make a call?'

'*Quién sabe?* I do not know, *Señorita*. Even if they are

working, you would first have to use the *Señor*'s radio
. . . I do not know how it operates, do you?'

'No,' Megan admitted, 'I've never used one. Tell me,
Maria, are those keys hanging on the peg board over
there for the Land Rover?'

The woman nodded. '*Sí*. But *Señor* Porter did not
mention anything . . .'

Smiling reassuringly, ignoring Maria's worried face,
Megan crossed the room and took the keys from the
wall. 'He must have forgotten to tell you,' she said, the
lie slipping from her lips with an ease borne of desperation. 'I just have to go out for a while . . . don't worry,
Maria, I'll be back later.'

'But *Señorita*—where do you go?' The woman's voice
rose as Megan hurried past her and out of the kitchen.
'There is nowhere to drive to . . . Only Durango, and it
is hours from here . . .'

Back in her room, Megan fumbled open her backpack
and snatched a small notebook and pencil from its
depths. She scribbled a note to Cam, explaining nothing
except that she would pay someone in Durango to
deliver the car back to the ranch. Her hand wavered . . .
there was so much more to say, she thought, so much to
tell him.

'Don't be a fool,' she muttered under her breath,
stuffing the pad and pencil back where they belonged
and propping the note against the lamp on the bedside
table. 'What can you possibly tell him that will change
the truth?

The Land Rover was parked where Cam had left it
when he'd brought her here. Someone had refuelled it,
she noticed, probably from the tank that fed the generator. The engine started easily, and Megan shifted it into
gear. She glanced into the rear-view mirror as she drove
off. Cam and his men were nowhere in sight. She could

see only Maria, standing in the doorway, gazing after her with an expression of concern on her face.

She drove along the narrow road leading from the ranch as quickly as possible. Cam had turned on to it from a slightly wider one—she remembered that clearly. But the road and the forest through which it knifed looked entirely different by daylight. Travelling as they had, through the black night, it had been impossible to pick up any landmarks. Still, there was nothing to worry about . . . after all, how many roads could there be in this wilderness? It would be virtually impossible to take the wrong one.

Two hours later, Megan wiped beads of perspiration from her brow and admitted that taking the wrong road might not only have been possible but probable. In fact, to call this overgrown cut through the trees a road was an overstatement. She had taken a turn-off about half an hour from the ranch, and had been trying to convince herself for the past several miles that it had been the correct one. Now, with the road petering off into a rut and the trees crowding in over the Land Rover, she was forced to acknowledge that she'd made a mistake. There was no way to turn back; the road simply wasn't wide enough to manoeuvre the car. Cautiously, she drove on, bouncing into potholes and praying that the Rover's ground clearance was high enough so the rocks in the road wouldn't puncture anything vital. The road had been bending back on itself for some time; perhaps it would connect back to the road leading to the ranch. With a groan of dismay, Megan braked, shifted into neutral and shut off the ignition. The way ahead was completely blocked by a fallen pine.

Now what? she thought miserably. She had travelled at least ten miles from the turn-off. She opened the door and stepped outside. It was so quiet here, she thought, looking around at the forest pressing in around her. Well, there was nothing particularly ominous about silence, she told herself firmly. At least it was still early in the day; there were hours of daylight left. If only the road were wider so that she could turn the Land Rover around.

With a sigh, she got back into the car. There was nothing to do except back up the way she'd come. Shifting into reverse, letting the clutch in slowly, Megan began inching her way back back along the rutted, narrow road. Within minutes, several hard jolts and thuds proved how little she could actually see of the winding road behind her.

A quarter of an hour later, her neck and arms aching from the strain of the constant backward manoeuvring, she was barely inching along a section of the road that seemed to have been half eroded by rain. It had been a difficult stretch when she drove it the first time; now, travelling backwards, it seemed virtually impassable. The Rover gave a sudden lurch, tilted alarmingly to the right, and stalled to a shuddering halt.

'Come on, sweetheart,' she whispered to the car as she restarted the engine and shifted into four-wheel drive. 'You can do it . . . all we need is some firm ground under us . . .'

The wheels spun furiously, but the Rover went nowhere. It tilted threateningly, even further to the right, its left side rising alarmingly with every spin. Finally, Megan turned off the ignition and slammed her hands against the steering-wheel in frustration.

'Double damn,' she muttered, wrenching open the door and clambering upwards out of the Rover. 'What now?'

She dropped to the road and scrambled around to the right side of the car. Both right wheels were embedded in mud hubcap deep; the entire left side of the vehicle was at least six inches off the ground.

A brightly plumaged bird dropped to the road several feet ahead and cocked its head, eyeing her warily. Satisfied that she presented no threat, it plucked an insect from the mud, swallowed the delicacy, and flew up on to the branch of a pine tree. Megan grimaced as the bird broke into a self-satisfied trill.

'Stop being so smug,' she muttered, taking her backpack from the car and hoisting it on her shoulders. 'If I could fly out of this mess, I'd sing, too.'

Well, she thought, there were two choices. Either she could tramp back along this same road or continue on ahead. Perhaps it made sense to go on for a while. After all, a road—even one such as this—must lead somewhere. And, at least, this direction led away from Cam. She settled the pack against her back and began walking.

She marched steadily onward, following the curving road, until the place where she'd left the Land Rover was lost to view. Her pace quickened when she spotted a small clearing. Her hopes soared. Perhaps this was the beginning of the road Cam had used to take her to the ranch. Her shoulders sagged under the weight of the pack and her steps faltered as she drew nearer. The clearing was nothing more than a space hacked out in the midst of entangling vines and trees, although there were signs of relatively recent use: a couple of empty wine bottles, dregs of ruby liquid still glistening in the bottom of each, lay before the remains of an extinguished campfire. There were a few empty beer bottles as well, these older than the wine bottles, if she were to judge by the soggy, unreadable labels still clinging to them. Somehow, these signs of human habitation were not reassuring; she found herself shuddering as she remembered Cam's warning that there were occasional bandits in the mountains. And the road, such as it had been, ended here.

Flattened plants and trodden grass seemed to indicate that there was a narrow footpath ahead. Fighting back the urge to look over her shoulder every other second, she decided to follow it. Whoever had left the bottles and campfire behind had come from somewhere; she thought it seemed logical that they had walked here from the road she was certain must be ahead. She could make the path out clearly as it wound ahead of her, and she tried to remember what she could of her childhood Girl Guide memories, orientating herself with the sun and the growth patterns of moss on some of the trees, until she was convinced that the pathway led in the general direction she wanted to take. And it seemed straighter than the road she'd driven . . . Megan glanced at her watch. Still early afternoon, she thought. Plenty of time to scout ahead for a while. She could always change her mind and head back to the narrow road where she'd left the Land Rover.

Following the path was easy at first. There were several deadfalls that had to be negotiated, and a couple of rocks to scramble over, but her progress was steady. Insects were a slight problem—tiny gnats circled her head and got into her eyes and nose once or twice—but she ignored them as best she could. It was difficult, once or twice, to decide just which way the path led. Vegetation seemed flattened in more than one direction, but each time she chose what appeared to be the more used path. At least, she told herself thankfully, her ankle wasn't bothering her, although it seemed to twinge once as she stumbled over an exposed tree root. She pushed the damp hair back off her forehead and glanced at her watch again. Frowning slightly, she shook her wrist and then raised it to her ear. Damn! The dumb thing had stopped working. And it read 2:30, although heaven only knew how long ago it had stopped.

Again, it occurred to her that it was terribly quiet here. It was almost abnormally quiet, she realised. What had happened to the bird calls she'd grown accustomed to? She could hear nothing but the persistent hum of the gnats as they hovered over her head. The feeling of unease swept over her again, and she fought it back. She'd cross this one last deadfall, the one blocking the path ahead from view, and if she hadn't reached the road by then, she'd go back.

Her heart seemed to skip a beat. The deadfall was an old one. It had created a slight depression in the ground when it fell, and the earth around it was bare of grass and slightly damp. There was a footprint, a pawprint, really, clearly outlined in the soft earth. Megan bent forward and ran her finger along the print.

'It could be a dog,' she whispered through dry lips. 'It could be . . .'

But she knew it wasn't. A long-ago course in mammal ecology had taught her that much. This was a bear print, a large one, and it contained claw marks. Black bears didn't leave that kind of print, she thought, as the hair on the back of her neck rose. Her eyes moved to the tree next to the fallen one and up along its trunk. They didn't leave claw marks that high off the ground, either. No small bear had left that calling-card behind. Only a grizzly could stand that tall.

'Oh my God . . .' Her whispered words caught in her throat. What a stupid fool she'd been. This was, indeed, a path through the forest. But no human feet had stamped it into the ground. It was a bear path—a grizzly path—and recently used, from the looks of the massive pawprint in the mud.

Megan turned and began to run back the way she'd

come. Her professor in the course on mammals had mentioned, almost as a conversational aside, that it was advisable to whistle or sing in grizzly country, that if the great creatures heard you, they might stay out of your way. That seemed like eminently sensible advice, she thought, but her throat and lips were dry and constricted with fear. She croaked out a few hesitant sounds and then gave up, concentrating her energies on getting back to the clearing, and the Land Rover beyond it, as quickly as possible.

Coming to one of the places where the pathway forked, she hesitated for a second and then plunged on. In a few hundred yards, it forked again and she paused, wondering which was the one to take, trying not to worry if she had taken the right one the first time. At least half an hour later, she drew up short. A solid wall of tall trees loomed ahead. Somewhere, at least a mile back, she'd made the wrong choice.

'Don't panic,' she warned herself, although it was meaningless advice. She retraced her steps, dimly aware that her ankle had begun to throb, until at last she reached the last fork. But the other pathway looked no more familiar than the first, and after a while, she stopped and slumped against a tree, her head bowed in despair. What now? she wondered. Her ankle was past the point of throbbing; it hurt with a steady, sharp stab of pain each time she put her weight on it. It was time to admit she had not the least idea where she was, nor the foggiest idea of how to get back to the Land Rover. And she'd been wandering around out here for hours: already, late afternoon shadows were beginning to creep into the forest, for day would end here sooner than in a cleared area, where the sun could spread its reassuring light until it set.

Exhausted, almost defeated, she eased the pack from

her aching shoulders and slumped to the ground. No one would look for her until tomorrow, if then. Cam would find her note and wait for the Land Rover to be returned to him, probably not expecting it until the next day or perhaps the day after. The best thing to do would be to eat one of the granola bars in her pack and then get some rest. In the morning, when the sun came up, she would start out fresh. There had to be a safe place to spend the fast-approaching night; sitting here, waiting for rescue in the middle of a grizzly path, was just plain stupid. She thought of climbing a tree for the night, but the lowest branches of the giants around her were easily fifteen feet off the ground. Well, she thought with a sigh, at least she could move off the bears' highway.

Resolutely, she picked up her pack and hobbled off the path and into the trees. Within minutes, she found herself in a glade. It wasn't much larger than a small bedroom, but it seemed free of animal scats or prints. Megan pulled off her pack and sank to the ground, leaning her back against a small boulder. At least it afforded some sort of protection, she thought, although she knew it was more psychological than physical. She opened the pack and dug through it until she found the granola bar. First things first, she told herself firmly, putting it aside and digging into the pack again. She sighed with relief as she drew out a flashlight and a book of matches. Switching on the light, she felt a small surge of comfort run through her. It was foolish to waste the battery while there was still the slightest touch of daylight, but the feeble glow made her feel less alone and frightened.

Propping the flashlight against the boulder, she got to her feet, wincing slightly as she put her weight on her injured ankle. There was plenty of brush for a fire scattered all around the small clearing, and she collected an armful of it, bringing it to the centre of the glade until she had enough to burn for a while. Her hands were trembling so badly that it took some effort to strike a match and light the kindling, but after a couple of unsuccessful tries, the wood caught and an orange flame sprang up. And just in time, she thought, repressing a shudder. The darkness of the forest was almost complete.

She sat down before the fire and pulled off her shoes. Almost immediately, her throbbing ankle felt better. The fire was blazing now, and she reached out for the flashlight and switched it off. My God, she thought, how dark it was. The trees surrounding her were black, ominous shapes towering overhead. She leaned back against the boulder, taking what little comfort she could from the sturdy feel of it against her back. Slowly, she began to pick out the night sounds of the forest. Above the faint drone of the insects, there were soft rustlings in the leaves. Megan shivered and drew her jacket more snugly around her. An animal called out once, faintly, in the distance, but the sound seemed magnified a hundred times over. She forced herself to look at the fire blazing before her, trying to ignore the shadows that loomed beyond. That was her safety net, her security blanket. No animal, not even a grizzly, would approach flame, would it? An image of the bottle-strewn clearing near the abandoned Land Rover flashed into her mind. A fire wouldn't keep away the men who'd camped there . . . in fact, it might even attract them . . .

What was that? Megan sat up straight, every nerve ending alert. There! She heard the sound again. She peered past the fire, into the forest, trying to see into the blackness. Something was moving through the trees, she was sure of it. Her breath seemed to catch in her throat. Slowly, never taking her eyes from the impenetrable darkness ahead, she reached for the flashlight. Gripping it tightly in her hand, she rose slowly to her feet. Whatever was coming was big and close. Trembling with fear, she edged away from the fire and around the side of the boulder.

'Stay back,' she yelled. 'Go on—get out of here.'

An enormous dark shadow moved into the clearing. Megan had barely switched on the flashlight before it was upon her. Wildly, she swung the heavy light in front of her, wielding it like a club, but a hand closed around her wrist and the light fell to the ground at her feet. Sobbing, she raised her other hand, clenching it into a fist, and began to pound at the intruder, but strong fingers with the grip of steel manacles closed around her wrist and held her fast. It was a bandit, she thought with mounting terror, not a bear. But which was worse? Which would hurt her the least? Which would . . .

'Megan, stop it. Megan, it's Cam . . .' The hands were drawing her closer, and she shook her head from side to side, fighting against a strength greater than her own, pounding uselessly on a hard unyielding chest, struggling to break free. 'You're safe, darling, do you understand? Megan, please, listen to me.'

'Cam?' she whispered unbelievingly. 'Cam?' His grip on her wrists loosened and she pulled one hand free and touched his face. Like a sightless person reading a book written in Braille, she ran her fingers along his firm jaw, his straight nose, until at last she touched the rough wool of his shirt. 'Oh, Cam,' she sighed, falling against him with a shudder. 'I thought you were . . . I can't believe it. How did you find me?'

His arms closed around her and he drew her trembling body against the hard warmth and safety of his.

'I found the Land Rover,' he mumbled, his breath warm against her ear. 'And then I followed your trail

—God, Megan, I thought I'd lost you forever. You were on a grizzly path—when I think of what might have happened—' He pushed her away from him and grasped her shoulders. 'What the hell were you doing?' he demanded angrily, shaking her limp body. 'What kind of stunt was that to pull?'

'I . . . I was leaving you,' she whispered, the words trembling out without thought or plan. 'I was going to go away before I hurt you, Cam.'

'Hurt me?' he repeated. 'What are you talking about? Finding that note hurt me, Megan. Finding that abandoned car, knowing you were lost out here in this forest—that hurt me.' His voice rose with anger and he shook her again. 'You could have died on this mountain, damn you!'

She closed her eyes as tears began to spill down her cheeks. 'Don't be angry, please,' she whispered. 'Please, Cam, don't hate me.'

'Hate you?' He drew a ragged breath and then his arms closed around her once more. 'You don't understand,' he whispered. 'God, Megan . . .' His hand moved up into the silken tangle of her hair and he laid her head against his chest. 'How could I ever hate you?' he murmured.

She wanted to tell him that someday, someday if —when—he learned the truth about her, he'd know how, but it was impossible, not while he held her this closely, not while she could hear the rapid beat of his heart and feel the warmth of his breath against her ear.

'It would have been better if you hadn't found me,' she whispered finally, her words muffled against him. 'So much better . . .'

'Don't say that,' he said angrily. 'You don't know what you're talking about.'

'I do,' she murmured, 'oh, I do. Because now that

you're here, now that I'm in your arms . . .' She raised her tear-streaked face to his and the breath caught in her throat. 'Cam,' she whispered, 'Cam . . .'

He bent his head and his lips met hers. She knew at once that everything she had feared, everything she had fled from, was upon her. It was too late to run away from what was happening to her, too late to regret what she knew must eventually follow the wild abandon of this moment. Desire could be fought against, but this was much more than that. She loved him, she thought wildly . . . she, who had never believed she would love again, knew now that she had never really loved before.

With a moan, she coiled her arms around his neck, opening her mouth to his, moulding the warm softness of her body to the steely hardness of his until she felt as if his chest and thighs would be imprinted on her forever. With fingers that still trembled, but no longer from cold or fear, she stroked the dark, thick hair at the nape of his neck, sighing as his mouth left hers and touched the long column of her throat.

'Wait,' he whispered in a voice thick and husky with desire. She drew back and watched as he drew a revolver from his belt.

'I don't want the others to go on searching,' he said, as he fired it twice into the air. 'That's the signal we agreed on if you were found safe.' He reached out and took her hand in his, drawing her slowly towards him again. 'Now,' he breathed, and she came into his arms as if she had waited for this moment all her life.

'You do want me, don't you?' he murmured against her mouth. 'I was right, wasn't I?'

'Yes,' she whispered without shame, 'yes, I want you. But . . .'

'There aren't any "buts",' he said, and when she felt the touch of his mouth against hers, she knew he was

right. There was nothing to think of, nothing to know
except the sweet taste of him, the feel of his lips as they
conquered hers. The vertigo she had felt with him in the
meadow returned, only now she knew it for the soft,
drowning pleasure it was. With a sigh, she tilted her head
back as his mouth left hers and moved to her neck,
leaving a blazing trail of kisses along her skin. He
whispered her name as he bent her back in his arms and
ran his hand up her body, until at last he cupped her
breast. She trembled as he kissed the soft rise of flesh at
the open vee of her chamois shirt, and then she felt his
fingers fumble at the buttons. The shirt fell open and he
eased it gently from her shoulders and tossed it aside.

'I want to make love to you, Megan,' he said softly.

'Yes,' she whispered in a low voice, 'yes . . .'

She felt the light touch of his hands as he opened her
lace bra and drew it from her. 'God, how beautiful you
are,' he groaned. 'How beautiful . . .'

Her eyes opened and she looked at his face. In the
flickering flames of the fire, there was an intensity about
it that was at once frightening and exciting. She shuddered as his hands moved slowly up from her waist and
cupped her breasts. A small sound escaped her as his
fingers moved upwards and stroked against her waiting,
hardened nipples. She reached out to him, wanting to
touch him as he was touching her, but he shook his head.

'There's time,' he whispered, and his husky words
sent a shiver up her spine. 'We have all the time in the
world, love. I want to look at you, Megan—I want to
touch you, taste you . . .'

She felt him fumbling at her waistband, and heard the
hiss of the zipper on her jeans as he pulled it open. Her
clothing seemed to fall from her body as if she were
shedding a skin long outgrown, and then she felt the
warmth of the fire on her naked skin. His hands were

moving over her with a touch as soft as his kisses, stroking her softly and bringing her flesh to eager life.

'You're beautiful,' he said again, and she sighed, knowing that, at this moment, it was so. Cam knelt before her and pulled the jeans down to her feet, the pain in her ankle forgotten as she stepped free of their encumbrance. She touched her hand to the dark head bent before her and he looked up at her and smiled. A blinding bolt of love and need shot through her such as she'd never known during the years of her marriage to Jeff.

He leaned back on his heels and looked at her, his eyes searing her flesh as they travelled over her, until at last she could stand no more.

'Cam, please,' she whispered, blushing as much from the intensity of his gaze as from the desire she felt for him. She reached out to him, and he caught her hand in his and brought it to his lips, turning it so that his mouth touched her palm. Slowly, his eyes never leaving hers, he pulled off his shirt. The firelight danced over his muscled shoulders and chest, casting a darker bronze glow over the tanned, supple skin. She felt her legs begin to tremble as he opened his belt, and then, finally, he reached out to her and took her hand.

'Come to me, Megan,' he murmured softly, drawing her towards him. 'Come to me . . .'

'Yes,' she sighed, kneeling before him, 'yes . . .'

As he drew her into his arms, she could only wonder which was the hotter: the heat of his skin against hers, or the fire blazing beside them. After a while, as his lips and body claimed hers, it became impossible to wonder about anything.

CHAPTER EIGHT

MEGAN fell asleep in Cam's arms, curled snugly against his chest. Some time in the misty, grey hour before dawn, she stirred and her lashes fluttered open. Cam's face was next to hers, his handsome, strong features softened and gentled by sleep. Softly, so as not to wake him, she raised herself on one elbow and propped her head on her hand.

When the night grew cold, they'd covered themselves with an assortment of sweaters and jeans pulled from her backpack, giggling like children as they tried to arrange the irregular heap of clothing over their bodies, until the laughter died, changing with quicksilver speed to something else as their hands touched each other, and her body had arched up to meet his in sweet, willing assent.

The heaped garments had fallen from him as he slept, and her eyes drifted over him, her glance lingering on his muscled arms and shoulders, the soft whorl of dark hair on his chest, his flat, hard stomach and long, strong legs. He was beautiful, she thought in surprise. She had never thought of a man in that way before, but then, she'd never looked at one in quite the same way. It seemed to her that every plane and angle of his face blended perfectly into the next. She reached out and touched his firm, sensuous mouth lightly with her finger, blushing as she remembered the feel of it on her skin. He murmured something in his sleep and rolled towards her, and his arm curved around her waist and drew her down beside him. With a sigh, Megan settled against him as if she'd always belonged there, closing her eyes as she heard the steady, soothing beat of his heart beneath her ear.

Everything that had happened in the past few days seemed impossible to believe. The ethics of her profession, her self-imposed and entirely comfortable celibacy since her divorce—all that had been cast aside for the man in whose arms she lay. Her guilt and anguish had been driven from her during the long hours of the night, only to return now as stealthily as the tiny animals moving on soft, delicate paws through the surrounding forest. How could she leave him now? she wondered, gazing at his face through half-opened eyes. And yet, it was not a question of 'could', was it? It was a question only of when and how . . . She stirred slightly and turned her head away from his as a sob caught in her throat.

'Megan?' He whispered her name sleepily and raised his head. 'Good morning,' he said, smiling down at her.

She turned towards him, not sure whether to weep with sorrow or fling her arms around his neck. Finally, her mouth curved upward in a slow smile and she sighed.

'Good morning,' she said softly. She struggled to an upright position and bent over him towards her backpack. 'Would you like some breakfast?' She flushed as he grinned wickedly. 'I only meant . . . there are some granola bars in my pack,' she said quickly. 'Here, take one. It's not much, but it's better than nothing.'

He grinned again as his hand reached out and cupped the full softness of her breast.

'That's an inadequate description of something so perfect, Megan.'

The rapid, heated response flooding through her body startled and dismayed her. She twisted away from his caress and tossed one of the granola bars into his lap.

'Cam, don't . . . It's almost daylight,' she said, desire slurring the words slightly.

He stared at her quizzically and then nodded his head. 'That's true,' he said solemnly, sitting up and running his hand through his hair. 'And we wouldn't want the bears to catch us like this, would we? After all, they might not approve.'

Despite herself, she began to smile. 'You know I didn't mean it that way . . .' Her smile faded and she glanced nervously over her shoulder.

He grinned lazily and pulled her towards him. 'I don't think we have to worry about it, Megan. As far as I know, bears haven't read Miss Manners' book on etiquette just yet.'

'But they could be right around here, couldn't they?' she insisted, fighting against the desire to let her body melt into his. 'Isn't that right?'

To her relief, Cam sighed and his hands dropped from her shoulders. 'Okay,' he murmured, 'I give up. We haven't seen or heard a bear all night, but you win, Megan. We'll clear out of here.' He tilted her face up to his and brushed her lips gently with his. 'But only because I want your undivided attention when I make love to you, understand?' he teased softly. 'Just keep that in mind when we get back to the ranch, woman. There aren't any bears to take your mind off things in my bedroom.' He got to his feet and pulled her up alongside him. 'Better get your clothes on fast,' he added with a grin. 'Otherwise, bears or no bears, I may change my mind.'

Cam put a makeshift bandage on her ankle before they left the clearing, although the throbbing in it had subsided. Much to her surprise and chagrin, the Land Rover was less than half a mile from where she'd given up looking for it the night before, and it took Cam only a few minutes to attach a cable to one of the towering pine trees alongside the road and winch the car free of the mud. He had no trouble negotiating the Rover backwards along the narrow, rutted road, and it seemed no time at all before they were out on the road leading to the ranch. Megan cleared her throat when she finally glimpsed the clearing ahead, and the low-slung house centred within it.

'I . . . I suppose you're wondering why I ran off that way,' she said hesitantly, and Cam looked at her and smiled.

'That's a strange thing to ask me now, isn't it? If I wanted the answer, I could have asked you that hours ago.'

She nodded her head and caught her lip between her teeth. 'Yes, I thought of that. Why haven't you asked me, Cam? I all but stole your car, drove it into a ditch, made you tramp through the woods searching for me, but you haven't said a word about any of it.'

'I don't have to, Megan. You see, I understand. I know why you ran away.'

Her breath caught in her throat as he spoke. 'You do?' she asked tensely. 'When did you find out?'

He drove into the clearing and brought the car to a stop. 'The night you helped me deliver the foal,' he said quietly, swivelling around in his seat towards her.

'You knew and you still wanted me?' she murmured in disbelief. 'I don't understand, Cam. How could you? Didn't it change what you felt for me?'

He smiled and shook his head. 'It only made me want you more,' he said. 'Is that so hard to understand?' He slid across the seat towards her and cupped her face in his hands. 'I'd only just realised that it was okay to want someone again, to admit my own feelings to myself. Why wouldn't I have recognised that same awakening confusion in you?'

For a few moments, Megan had felt as if a weight were

lifting from her chest. Now, as she listened to his words and looked into his eyes, it returned with a crushing force.

'What do you mean?' she finally managed to whisper.

Cam slid his hands down her shoulders and leaned his forehead against hers. 'It isn't terribly complicated,' he said quietly. 'It's true, my marriage wasn't a good one, but it didn't start out that way. I cared for Sally, Megan. When things began to fall apart for us, when I realised what I felt for her was more pity than love, it hurt. I would have divorced her if she hadn't been . . .' His breath hissed through his teeth and he shook his head. 'I lived through a bad marriage,' he said flatly. 'And I suffered through the dissolution of it, just as you did.'

'But I haven't told you anything about my marriage, Cam. How can you know what it was like for me?'

His hands tightened on her and he lifted his head and gazed into her eyes. 'I know,' he said firmly. 'It's written in your face, in that sadness in your eyes . . .'

She shook her head and tears gathered on her lashes. 'You don't understand . . . Yes, my marriage was a bad one. And I still suffer when I think about it. But that's not why I ran away from you, Cam. I . . .'

'You were afraid, just as I was, Megan. Afraid to want somebody again, really want somebody—not just for an evening, or a week, but . . .'

'Cam, please . . . you've got to listen to me . . .'

'I know I'm rushing things,' he interrupted quickly. 'I know everything is happening too fast for you, Megan. But I couldn't just sit back and let what I'd found slip away. When I took you in my arms the other night, I knew that you were afraid of caring, of giving, just as I was.' His voice lowered to a husky whisper. 'And I was right, wasn't I? You were afraid to give in to what was happening between us, because of where it might lead.'

She lowered her head and tears streamed down her cheeks. 'Yes, you were right,' she said miserably. 'But that's not all of it, Cam. It's so much more complicated than that . . .'

He tilted her chin up and stared into her eyes. 'When you're ready to talk about it, I'll listen,' he said quietly. 'Although I don't know what you could tell me about that ex-husband of yours that would make sense. Any man who'd give you up must be a fool. At least, it couldn't have been the usual "other woman" kind of thing. No one would choose another woman after having known you.'

She began to smile in spite of her tears. 'You see how wrong you can be?' she murmured. 'There was another woman—Jeff's mother.'

Cam grinned as he gently wiped the tears from her cheeks. 'Score one for me,' he said lightly. 'Both my folks died when I was just a kid.'

'Cam, that's awful,' Megan said, laughing and crying at the same time. 'Anyway, it wasn't that simple.' Her laughter died and she leaned her head against his shoulder. 'Jeff wanted children . . .'

His arms seemed to tense around her. 'And you didn't?' he asked finally.

'I always wanted a child,' she said softly. 'Even when I knew the marriage was a disaster.' She took a deep breath and confessed what she had never told anyone in the years since her divorce. 'I couldn't get pregnant,' she murmured, choking on the admission. 'I don't really know why, but I couldn't. I wanted to adopt a child, but Jeff said . . . he said he couldn't love another man's child, that a real woman . . . a real woman could give life . . .' Her voice broke and tears flooded her eyes.

Cam's arms tightened around her until she could hardly breathe. 'If I ever have the misfortune to meet that bastard . . .' He drew back and kissed her damp eyelids. 'You see? I was right. You ran away from me because you've been hurt before.'

She drew a deep breath before answering. 'Life is full of hurt, Cam. There's no guarantee each of us won't be hurt again.'

'Megan,' he said firmly, 'I'm not asking for any promises. I'm not even offering any. It's too soon, and we're both too wary. All I'm saying is that we'd be fools to walk away from each other now. Not when we've just found each other.' He smiled and brushed the hair back from her face. 'You're a scientist,' he said teasingly. 'You can't argue with that kind of impeccable logic.'

'But I'm not . . .' she began, and he grinned.

'Not logical? Well, in that case, I'll have to resort to something underhanded.' He reached out and snatched the keys from the ignition. 'I'm going to hide these,' he said, burying them in his pocket. 'Let's see, what else is there?'

He frowned in mock concentration and she began to smile. 'Cam, be serious . . .'

'Ah, the radio. Maria tells me you asked her about it. Well,' he grinned, tweaking her nose gently, 'you can forget about that avenue of rescue, my fair maiden. By the time you figure out how to use it, it will be too late.'

'Too late for what?'

He clasped her in his arms and buried his face against her throat. 'Too late to stop me from ravishing you again,' he growled.

'You're insane,' she laughed, pushing free of his encircling arms.

'And starved,' he added, laughing along with her. 'What you've done to my appetite is indecent. But Maria will understand. She'll take one look at the two of us and cook up a batch of *huevos rancheros*, and tortillas, and pancakes, and sausage . . .'

'She's not getting a glimpse of me until I've showered and changed,' Megan said positively, opening the car door and stepping outside. 'I must look as if I've been . . .'

She broke off in embarrassed confusion and Cam smiled. 'Yes, you do,' he murmured. 'And it becomes you.'

She turned away from him and trotted to the house, slipping through the door as quickly and quietly as possible. The foyer and hallway were empty, and she breathed a sigh of relief when she reached her room. Somehow, the last thing she wanted to see just now was Maria's trusting face.

When she entered the kitchen half an hour later, Maria was beaming with delight.

'*Señor* Porter tells me you have decided to stay with us,' she said cheerfully. 'I am pleased, *Señorita*.'

'*Gracias*, Maria. Is he out on the terrace?'

'Ah, no, not yet, *Señorita*. He is still dressing . . . He suggested you have some coffee and wait here for him.' Her dark eyes flashed with amusement as she handed Megan a steaming mug. 'He said you might wish to start breakfast without him, as you are very hungry this morning.'

Megan blushed and shook her head. 'No, not very,' she said carefully. 'I can wait until he's ready.'

The housekeeper sighed and eased herself into a chair opposite Megan. '*Sí*, well, I hope it is not too long a wait. He took his new script into the bedroom with him . . . Sometimes, he forgets everything but the need to study that.' She smiled shyly at Megan and shrugged her shoulders. 'Although, I suspect that will not happen to him this time, *Señorita*.'

'New script?' Megan asked quickly, to cover her embarrassment. 'I didn't know he was preparing for another film.'

'Ah, *sí*, he is. He brought it here with him when he arrived. Always, he loses himself in—how do you say —the preparation, *sí*?'

Megan nodded her head. 'Yes, so I gather. He told me that he got interested in ranching because of a part in a film.'

'Yes, so Andres has told me. That was before I came to work for him, of course. But in the years since then, I have seen him do this many times.' She smiled and leaned back in her chair. 'Sometimes, it is funny, what goes on here. He is so serious about his roles . . .'

'That's what makes him such a fine actor, I guess,' Megan said thoughtfully, sipping at her coffee, 'getting into the character he's going to play.'

Maria sighed. 'But sometimes it is too much, *Señorita*. When he was to play a skier, he learned to ski—not just to ski, but to race—and he broke his leg. Oh, yes, he was many weeks in a cast, *Señorita*. And last year, he made a film about prison.'

'Yes, I saw it. He was terrific, Maria.'

'*Sí*, but to prepare, he stayed out of the sun—to not look too healthy, you understand?—and he went on a diet and lost much weight. No good, a man as big as the *Señor*, to get so thin.'

Megan tried not to smile at the motherly concern in the other woman's voice. 'Well, he gained it back, didn't he? I guess he thought the part was worth it.'

The housekeeper smiled. '*Sí*, I am certain you are right, *Señorita*. And some of the times, it is for the best, how do you say, for the art.'

'I'm sure it is,' Megan agreed, returning the woman's

smile. 'Is that why he learned to fly his own plane? For a part he was going to play?'

Maria shook her head and her smile faded. 'No, no, not for a part. That was after he bought Las Montanas en Cielo, *Señorita*. It became necessary for him to get back and forth quickly, without others knowing . . . there was a problem, you see, and . . .'

She squirmed uncomfortably and Megan reached across the table and patted her hand.

'It's okay,' she said quietly. 'I know about his wife. He told me. I guess she had a lot of problems and needed him to be with her.'

The older woman's dark eyes met hers in surprise. 'He told you of her? I am glad to hear it.' She glanced down at the table and wiped at a faint spot on its gleaming surface. 'What did he tell you, *Señorita*?'

'That she wasn't well . . . that she died in a terrible accident.' She look at the woman's bent head and frowned. 'Why, Maria? Is there more to it than that?'

The housekeeper got up and turned towards the refrigerator. 'I am certain the *Señor* will be ready for breakfast soon,' she said, busying herself with taking things out of it. 'I think I shall make *huevos rancheros* and *chorizo*—sausage, *Señorita*. Also some bacon. I know it is in here somewhere . . .'

'Is something wrong, Maria? Have I said something to upset you?'

'No, no, of course not. It is simply that it is getting late.'

Puzzled, Megan watched the housekeeper in silence, and then got up from the table and poured herself more coffee.

'Do you like working for *Señor* Porter?' she asked, hoping to ease the tension that seemed to have suddenly descended on the kitchen. 'It must be lonely for you, all the way out here.'

'Lonely?' Maria laughed as she arranged sausages in a cast-iron skillet. 'I grew up in these mountains, *Señorita*. I am used to it.'

'Still, this ranch is so big . . . and the house must be very empty when *Señor* Porter is away.'

'He is away only when necessary,' the woman said stiffly.

'I'm sure he is,' Megan said quickly, wondering what it was that had upset the housekeeper. 'But it's such a big house for one man . . . Does he ever have guests?'

Maria slammed a cover on the skillet and turned to face Megan. 'I am certain the *Señor* can answer these questions for you better than I can,' she said sternly. 'Now, if you will excuse me, I have breakfast to prepare. If you will go out to the terrace, I am sure *Señor* Porter will join you in a few minutes.'

'Maria . . .' Megan's voice was bewildered and apologetic. 'Have I offended you? I'm sorry, really. It's just that I . . . I only want to know more about Cam—about *Señor* Porter. I . . .'

The housekeeper shrugged her shoulders and nodded her head. '*Sí*. But it is not for me to explain him to you.' Her voice softened and a strange look of compassion came into her eyes as she looked at Megan. 'He must explain himself, *Señorita*. Only he can do that.'

CHAPTER NINE

MEGAN looked up from the leather-bound notebook in her lap and smiled at Cam as he bent and kissed her forehead.

'You're back,' she said happily, shifting over to make room for him beside her on the chaise longue. 'I'm so glad.'

He grinned as he sat down and put his arm around her. 'I told you I wouldn't be gone very long. I bet you hardly missed me.'

She closed the notebook and leaned her head against his shoulder. 'I missed you every minute,' she assured him. 'You've been gone all morning . . . four hours and twenty-five minutes, to be precise,' she added, glancing at her watch and then smiling at him. 'You should have let me ride up into the meadow with you.'

'And risk hurting that ankle again?' He shook his head and brushed his lips against her forehead. 'I told you I wanted you to rest it until it's fully healed, Megan.'

'And I did, all day yesterday.'

'Stop arguing with me, woman,' he laughed, hugging her against him. 'Anyway, I know how you women are—you need time alone to polish your nails and fix your hair and paint your faces.' He grinned as she struck him lightly with her hand.

'Do you see any paint or polish on me?' she demanded. 'And there isn't a hairdresser in the world who wouldn't gag at the sight of me.'

His eyes lingered on her shining face and cloud of loose, gleaming chestnut hair and he smiled.

'They'd be choked with envy,' he murmured, tucking a stray curl behind her ear. 'I've seen actresses work at their make-up for hours and still not look as lovely as you.'

A pink blush that was part embarrassment and part pleasure spread over her cheeks, and she buried her face in the crook of his neck.

'My Irish grandmother would adore you,' she whispered. 'She thought you had to come from the Emerald Isle to do so well at spreading the blarney.'

'It's the truth,' he said solemnly, although his blue eyes were alive with laughter. 'Would I lie?'

She looked into his face and smiled shyly. 'I hope not,' she said lightly.

No, she thought, settling back into the curve of his arm, no, he wouldn't lie, although the feeling that he was holding something back persisted. The peculiar conversation she'd had with Maria the day before yesterday had left her puzzled and vaguely disturbed.

She cast a sidelong glance at Cam's face as he sat beside her. Perhaps Maria had only meant to imply that his wife's death might have been a suicide . . . after all, Maria had no way of knowing that Cam had already told her that. And then there was the strange way she'd reacted to Megan's question about other guests visiting the ranch. Maria had seemed so evasive, so uncomfortable . . . If the conversation had taken place when Megan had first arrived at Las Montanas en Cielo, when Cam was her quarry and not the man she'd fallen in love with, such cryptic responses would have set off a hundred other questions. Did he bring women to the ranch? Had he done so before his wife's death? Was that why the marriage had failed and Sally Porter been driven to such despair?

Megan closed her eyes. Those questions were

meaningless now. Cam was not the sort of man to do those things. He'd spoken of his wife with pain and regret . . . and he led a life here, in the Sierra Madres, that could almost be described as hermit-like in its secluded isolation. Perhaps Maria had merely been warning her that his marriage had left him emotionally scarred, or that there had been one or two women whom he'd brought to this place in the years since. Yes, Megan thought suddenly, that would make sense. She knew the marriage, and his wife's terrible death, had wounded him. He had told her so himself. If, in his loneliness, he'd brought someone to spend a few days at Las Montanas en Cielo with him in the past, what did that matter now? She turned her head slightly and looked at him through half-closed eyes. He was young and virile—a hermit, perhaps, but not a monk. And Maria, the great romantic, probably hoped Cam would tell her all this before she heard it from someone else . . .

Megan sighed as his arm tightened around her. Once a reporter, always a reporter, she thought, gently chiding herself for looking for dark secrets where there were none. She was the one with the secret, not he. And hers was the sort that could destroy everything.

'A penny for your thoughts,' he said softly, bending his dark head towards hers. 'You're so quiet, Megan. Is something troubling you?'

'No,' she said quickly, forcing herself to smile at him. 'Really, Cam, I'm fine.' He returned her smile, but there was still a question in his eyes, and she looked away from him with a stab of guilt. 'Well, actually, I was wondering . . .' she said hurriedly, trying to change the topic, 'this script I was reading while you were gone this morning —it's a couple of years old.' She picked up the leather notebook and glanced at him. 'I remember this film —you were wonderful in it.'

He ran his hand up her neck and ruffled her hair. 'I thought you didn't have much time for films,' he teased.

She felt the same sharp twinge of guilt again. 'I don't,' she assured him. 'But everyone said how great this picture was, so I went to see it. But . . .'

'But now that you've read the script, you're going to tell me how you would have done the part,' he teased, grinning at her.

'No, God no,' she said, laughing. 'All I meant was, I found a whole stack of scripts in the library. But where's your newest one? Maria said you were studying for a new film—what's it about?'

'My lips are sealed,' he said solemnly. 'I can't tell you, Megan.'

A smile tugged at the corners of her mouth. 'You can't tell me?' she repeated, and he nodded. 'Why? Is it a state secret? Have you signed an oath?'

He smiled and shook his head. 'Only with myself. I never let anybody see a new script until I'm sure I understand the character I'm to play.'

'But what's it about? You can tell me that much, at least, can't you?'

'You'll know soon enough,' he promised. 'I'll tell you all about it in a couple of days.'

'I'm disappointed,' she said, a teasing tone in her voice. 'Here I am, watching the creative process at work, waiting for you to do whatever it is you must do to get ready for this role, and what do I see happening? Nothing—absolutely nothing. Didn't you tell me you study a new part by researching for it?'

'Didn't you tell me you wanted to see how our new foal is doing?' he parried, getting to his feet and pulling her up with him. 'Is your ankle up to a walk to the stable?'

'My ankle is fine,' she said eagerly. 'I told you that. I'd

love to do something besides sit here, basking in the sun like an invalid.'

He smiled and took her hand in his. 'Okay, then. Let's go say hello to Bonnie and her baby.'

The mare and her foal were frolicking in a small paddock near the stable area, kicking up their heels as they romped across the grass. Megan leaned against the split-rail fence, smiling with pleasure as she watched the two animals. Bonnie had overcome her initial reluctance and become a patient, devoted mother, she noted. And the little foal was thriving. She glanced at Cam and her smile broadened as she remembered the night of the filly's birth and the closeness she and Cam had forged through those long hours. It was a closeness that had grown and sweetened during the past days, she thought. What would happen when she told him the truth about herself? If only she had the courage to admit everything . . .

'There's that same look on your face again,' he said suddenly. 'Some shadow that clouds your eyes . . . What is it, Megan? Aren't you happy?' His arm tightened protectively around her waist.

She covered his hand with hers and squeezed it lightly. 'Of course I am,' she said quickly. 'Why wouldn't I be?'

'I suppose it's not easy for you, stuck away here in the middle of nowhere, is it? You're not doing the job you came all this way to do . . .'

'I don't want to do it,' she said, giving the words such forceful impact that he arched an eyebrow in surprise. 'I mean, it doesn't seem very important now, Cam,' she added.

'Still, you don't strike me as someone who likes to sit idle for too long. And I've neglected you a bit, haven't I? Going off to that canyon to check on the horses this morning, riding fence with Andres yesterday . . .'

Megan rubbed her head against his chin. 'You had work to do. I understand that. But I could have gone along today, at least. Really, Cam—I know you're worried about my ankle, but it's fine.'

He moved his hand up to her shoulder and turned her towards him. 'Look, I have a terrific idea. I have something on for tomorrow. I was going to change it, but now I think it might be perfect left as is. You can come with me, Megan. You won't have to ride or do much walking, and the change of scene might do you some good.'

'If it means being with you, it will. But I don't understand . . .'

He cupped her face in his hands and smiled at her. 'It means you'll get a chance to see bright lights and people and shops . . . We can even buy you something to wear besides those jeans of yours.'

Megan frowned and shook her head. 'I still don't know what you're talking about. Are you driving into Durango?'

He grinned and kissed her forehead. 'Better than that. I'm supposed to meet my manager in Acapulco for lunch. He's there on vacation, and it seemed a good time to work out some details about my next film. I was going to leave you here, meet him for a working lunch in a private lounge at the airport and fly right back, but now it occurs to me that going to Acapulco might be just what you need to lift your spirits.'

'Lift my spirits? Cam, I don't need anything except . . .' She swallowed hastily, suddenly too shy to finish the sentence.

'What's that?' he teased. 'Are you saying you'd rather spend tomorrow with Maria than with me?'

She smiled and leaned her head against his chest. 'No, of course not. I only meant that I'm content wherever you are.'

'Well, then, it's settled. I'm going to be in Acapulco, and you're coming with me. How does that sound?'

'It sounds wonderful. I've never been to Acapulco. I've heard all about it, of course. The beaches, the palm trees, the cliff divers . . .'

His arms tightened around her and he caressed her hair. 'I've got a terrific idea, Megan. Instead of coming straight back after my meeting, we'll stay over for the night.' He drew back and smiled down at her. 'Would you like that?'

'Stay over for . . .' She shook her head. 'But I thought you hated places like that, Cam,' she said before she could think. 'You know, places where you might be recognised and bothered.' Her heart seemed to skip a beat as she realised what she'd said. 'At least, I thought I'd read that somewhere,' she added quickly.

She let out her breath when he smiled. 'You probably did. Whatever journalist wrote that managed the truth once in his life, at least.'

'Cam, they don't always lie . . .'

'Not always,' he said quickly. 'Sometimes they only distort and twist . . . But never mind all that, Megan. I can make arrangements at a place you'll like, a place where we won't be bothered. Anyway, I'm willing to risk it. I want to show you the Pacific Ocean, hold you in my arms while the sun sets over a secluded beach, drift through hibiscus blooms in our own private pool . . .'

Megan laughed and burrowed closer to him. 'Flowers? In our own pool? It sounds absolutely decadent —and absolutely lovely.'

'Then that's settled,' he said briskly. 'Come on; we'll go back to the house and I'll call Acapulco.'

'So,' she said archly, smiling up at him, 'the telephone lines are working again, are they? And just how long were you going to wait to tell me that, hmm?'

He grinned down at her and took her hand in his. 'I didn't even think of it,' he said. 'After all, we don't need to call for a taxi to take you away from here now, do we?'

Moments later, she stood quietly beside him, watching as he switched on his radio and set the various dials and switches. If only there were a real telephone here, she thought, one she could use quickly and privately to call New York. It would be a call that would puzzle and anger her editor, but one that must be made. She would tell Marian that she had lost Cam south of Durango, that she had no idea where he'd gone, and that she was staying on in Mexico for a long-needed vacation. That was the part Marian wouldn't accept easily, she knew, not with the Dr Dan story still waiting to be written. It would be out of character for her, but Marian would have no choice but to accept it. And if she asked when Megan would come back to New York or, even worse, demand her immediate return, what then? Megan sighed as Cam reached up and took her hand in his, drawing her closer to him as he sat before the radio. She knew her answer. She would stay here, with him, even if it meant losing her job, even though the future was still uncharted and darkened by what she must tell him about herself. Perhaps the time would be right in Acapulco. Perhaps there he would say that he loved her, put into words what she had so far only sensed, and then she would feel secure enough to tell him everything, to beg for his understanding . . .

She listened as he repeated his call letters over the air, smiling a bit when he whispered an apology to her as he waited for his contact in the village to put him through to the operator.

'This system takes a while,' he murmured. 'It's not the fastest way to make a simple telephone call.'

He broke off in mid-sentence and hunched over the

microphone on the table before him.

'*Sí*,' he said, '*sí. Las Brisas, en Acapulco. Gracias.*'

Finally, the connection was made, and Cam winked at her in relief. '*Buenos días*,' he said, and went on in a perfect Spanish she could barely follow. All she was certain of was that he was speaking with someone he knew, arranging for hotel reservations. When at last he switched off the radio, he sat back in his chair and grinned.

'We're all set. Our suite will be ready and waiting for us tomorrow, and the manager has promised to make the arrangements so carefully that no one gets wind of it.' His blue eyes sparkled with mischief. 'I'll bet you never checked into a hotel as Mrs Smith, did you?'

'No,' she laughed, 'I can't say that I ever did. You don't think that's really going to work, do you? As soon as people see you, they'll know who you are.'

'There's one great advantage to places like Acapulco, Megan. They've used to dealing with people like me. If you want to make headlines, the hotel management is agreeable to the publicity. If you don't, they'll help you keep a low profile.' His hands spanned her narrow waist and drew her towards him. 'I know this is hard,' he said quietly. 'All this planning on ways to avoid the public eye, but I prefer it this way.'

'Nothing is hard, as long as I'm with you,' she answered quickly. 'We don't have to go, if you don't want to.'

'But I do,' he insisted. A muscle in his jaw tensed and his eyes seemed to darken. 'I can't expect you to shut yourself off from the rest of the world just for me, Megan.'

'Cam, I don't feel shut off. I'm happy just being with you. I told you that.'

'Yes, you did. But the world—the real world—is out

there, past the mountains and canyons. It's foolish to deny it and hide from it forever, isn't it?' His voice was low and urgent, and she had the feeling he was saying more than she understood. Suddenly, he grinned and stood up. 'Besides, we'll be out of Acapulco before any reporters pick up our trail. By the time they come looking for me, we'll be safely back at Las Montanas en Cielo.'

Megan bowed her head and nestled it under his chin. 'You make them sound like hounds running a fox to ground,' she said softly. 'Surely they aren't all that bad.'

'That's what I used to think,' he muttered. 'Until Sally . . . my wife . . . I told you how it was, how the dirt she read about me tormented her, warped her mind, until . . .'

She raised her head and placed her hand lightly over his mouth. 'Don't,' she said quickly. 'Please, don't talk about it. I know how it hurts you, Cam. But you know that couldn't have been all of it. You told me yourself that she was—what was your word?—unstable, vulnerable. Surely not everyone who reads gossip about her husband ends up that way.'

'No,' he admitted finally, 'you're right.'

A faint spark of hope ignited within her. 'Anyway, not all the stuff written about you has been like that, has it? I mean, someone must have done some straight, honest reporting about you at some time or another.'

'If they write anything about my private life it isn't reporting any more,' he said grimly. 'It's nothing but an invasion of privacy when they print things about my life off-screen.'

'But the public is interested, Cam. People want to know what makes you tick.'

'Even if I agreed with that,' he said, his face darkening, 'it would still come to the same thing. Magazines and newspapers only print what sells, Megan, and what sells best is innuendo and scandal. If they can't dredge any up, they create it.'

His growing agitation snuffed out the struggling ember of hope that had briefly come to life. She reached up and smoothed back his dark hair.

'Okay,' she said softly, 'if that's how you see it, I won't argue. But then why take me to Acapulco tomorrow? Why run the risk of being photographed or written about, Cam? It's not worth it.'

'Yes it is,' he said, almost angrily. 'I've watched you these past few days, Megan. I sense something—a restlessness, a need . . .' He sighed and his voice gentled. 'You're young and lovely,' he said softly, his hand caressing her cheek. 'It isn't fair to expect you to hide yourself away like this.'

Guilt washed over her like darkness claiming the evening sky. What he sensed, she knew, was nothing but the depression she felt each time she thought of the lie she was living.

'Cam, for God's sake—have I said that? Have I even suggested it? I'm used to this kind of life—I told you that. If you're doing this for me, you needn't.'

'I'm doing it for myself,' he said cryptically, 'more than for you.'

She lifted her head from his chest and stared into his eyes. What private demons drove him so mercilessly, she wondered? They seemed, if anything, more powerful and destructive than her own. At last, she sighed and dropped her gaze.

'Whatever you say,' she whispered. 'Just so long as you know that being with you is all I need to be happy. Not anything else, Cam. Not anyone else.'

'Are you sure, Megan?'

She nodded her head. 'I never felt that before,' she

said quietly, searching for some way to reassure him.
'With Jeff—my husband—I always felt somehow
incomplete. Something always seemed to be lacking.'

'Is that why you wanted a child?'

'Maybe,' she admitted, touched that he would remember what she had said. 'But when we're together
. . .' She hesitated, afraid to say more than he was
prepared to hear. 'When we're together,' she went on, 'I
feel whole. There's no room for anything else, Cam. Not
anything.'

She raised her lashes and looked at him again, holding
her breath as she waited for him to answer, hoping that
the gift of love implicit in her whispered words would
make him tell her what she longed to hear. Instead, she
caught a strange expression on his face, a curious flatten-
ing and narrowing of his mouth. I've gone too far, she
thought quickly. He's not ready to fall in love, to get past
his old wounds. She forced herself to smile and relax in
his arms.

'Still,' she said, making her words sound bright and
cheerful. 'Mrs Smith wants you to know she's looking
forward to an idyll in Acapulco. Tell me, sir, is that
Smith spelled with a "y" or an "i"? And you could have
chosen a name with a bit more creativity, you know.
Something unusual, like Jones or Brown or . . .'

With relief, she saw the expression on his face change,
until finally he was smiling again.

'You can spell Smith any damned way you like,' he
murmured, his lips warm against her ear, 'just as long as
her given name is Megan.'

Her eyes closed as his mouth moved along her neck,
coming to rest against the pulse beating softly in the
hollow of her throat. Her arms tightened around him
and she pressed herself closer to him, flushing with
pleasure and happiness as she felt his body begin to

respond to hers. His hand tangled in the silken strands of hair that tumbled around her shoulders, and he bent her head back, his kisses trailing along her warming skin until his mouth touched the soft flesh above the closed buttons of her shirt.

'Cam,' she murmured, as his hands moved to open them, 'it's the middle of the day. What about Maria?'

The shirt parted under his questing fingers and he whispered to her shoulders. 'Maria believes in an honourable Spanish custom,' he said huskily. 'It's siesta time, love. It's time all good people took to their beds.'

The heat of a primordial sun seemed to rush through her. His hands moved softly, teasingly over her breasts, and then he lifted her up into his arms and covered her mouth with his.

'Where are you taking me?' she whispered as he strode out of the small radio room and walked purposefully down the hall. 'Cam?'

'To bed, Megan,' he growled. 'I just told you—it's siesta time.'

'But I'm not sleepy,' she murmured shamelessly, hiding her face in the crook of his neck.

His arms tightened around her as he stepped inside his bedroom and kicked the door closed behind him.

'I'm glad to hear it,' he said softly, easing her body down the full length of his as he stood her gently on the floor beside the bed. 'Because neither am I.'

Her last coherent thought, as his mouth took hers, was that she would put an end to her own duplicity as quickly as possible. The radio hadn't seemed as complicated as she'd expected. Cam wouldn't leave the ranch without giving some instructions to the vaqueros, and while he did, she'd use the radio to reach Marian in New York. She would say that Cam was nowhere to be found, that she was off the assignment. She would tell her, in fact, that she was quitting her job. And, when they left for Acapulco the next day, she would no longer be a reporter for *Sophisticate* magazine.

Megan drew Cam into her arms as his body moved over hers. When she told him everything, he would understand and forgive. For surely, certainly, this man who was claiming her, who had conquered her body and her soul, was more than her lover.

He was her love.

CHAPTER TEN

THE Lear jet soared over the harbour, swooping over the brilliant blue waters of Acapulco Bay like a hawk after a sparrow. A gentle wind seemed to froth the deep sapphire of the Pacific Ocean with white lace; beyond, high cliffs embraced stretches of white sand awaiting the caress of the sparkling water. Megan caught her breath as the plane banked above the rocky cliffs and levelled off.

'How beautiful it is, Cam,' she said happily. 'It's like a painting.'

Cam grinned at her as he throttled back the engines. 'I wanted you to see Acapulco from the ocean first. It is spectacular, isn't it?'

She nodded her head in agreement. 'Oh, yes—it certainly is. I can hardly wait to see it close up. How long until we land?'

'I've just got clearance from the control tower . . . only a few minutes more, Megan. Is your seat-belt tight? Okay then—just sit back and relax. We're heading down.'

Megan settled back into the co-pilot's seat and watched as the ground rose beneath them. It had taken longer to drive from Las Montanas en Cielo to the airport at Durango than it had to fly to Acapulco, and although she was eager to see the town sprawled below them, she was sorry the flight was almost over. She had never flown in a small plane before, and the sense of being part of the sky and the clouds was exhilarating. Cam loved flying—she knew that as soon as she climbed into the cockpit and looked at his face as he settled into the pilot's seat—and within minutes, his excitement and pleasure had communicated themselves to her. Sitting alongside him, soaring through the clear sky and white puffs of cloud, she felt happy and at peace Everything seemed perfect . . . well, almost everything, she thought, glancing at him. If she'd only been able to complete her call to Marian that day before . . .

As she'd expected, Cam had gone to speak with his vaqueros after dinner. She'd hurried to the radio-room, her heart pounding as she scurried past the kitchen, but Maria was busy singing lustily as she washed the dishes. With trembling fingers, she'd fumbled with the dials and switches on the radio, silently urging herself to hurry, to remember the order in which Cam had adjusted them, almost despairing of getting the set to work until, with a sudden hum and glow, the radio came to life. She'd whispered his call letters, following the procedure he'd used earlier to reach the village, sighing with relief when, at last, the other radio buff answered. Carefully, in broken Spanish, she explained that she wanted to place a call to New York. She gave him the telephone number and waited impatiently while he contacted the overseas operator.

'Hurry, please,' Megan whispered, aware of every slight sound in the house.

'Yes, I am trying, *Señorita*,' Cam's contact said politely. 'But it is a problem, you see. The operator informs me that all the lines are busy. Is it perhaps possible to place your call later this evening?'

In the end, Megan had given up, carefully turned off all the switches and tip-toed back to her room. Still, her conscience was lighter than it had been in days. She had severed herself from her job in her own mind, if not in actuality. She was still a journalist by profession, but not with the kind of magazine Cam hated. She could do other kinds of reporting, she told herself, straight news-writing, for instance, with a paper or newsweekly. Surely, he had nothing against that kind of reporter.

'Touchdown in just a few seconds,' he murmured, and she glanced at him and smiled.

She would call Marian the first chance she had, she thought, as the wheels of the Lear jet kissed the runway. While Cam spoke with his manager, she'd find the nearest telephone. And he'd understand, when she told him everything. The fact that she'd quit her job would be proof of her love.

They were greeted by a warm, tropical breeze tasting faintly of the sea. Cam carried their one suitcase and several handsomely wrapped boxes. She'd had nothing to pack suitable for a beach resort, and they'd spent a hectic hour in Durango that morning, rushing from shop to shop, picking out bathing suits and cool, cotton dresses, arguing over who would pay for them, until at last he'd laughed and stepped back.

'Okay, I give up,' he said, as she pulled her wallet from the pocket of her jeans. 'When we get to Acapulco, I'll hide your pesos before I take you shopping.'

As they entered the terminal, she felt scruffy and conspicuous in her faded denims and chambray shirt, and she began to wish she'd taken the time to change into one of the new dresses she'd bought. They seemed to be surrounded by beautiful, fashionably dressed women.

'Just look at me,' she whispered miserably. 'It'll be a miracle if they let me into the hotel like this.'

Cam grinned and slid his arm around her waist, drawing her against him. 'I think you look wonderful,' he said.

Megan shook her head. 'Then you're the only one

who does,' she murmured. 'I'm so out of place here; everyone is staring at me.' He chuckled and his arm tightened around her. 'Don't laugh, Cam,' she hissed. 'They are—they're all looking at . . .' The words caught in her throat and she blushed with humiliation. 'My God,' she said in wonder, 'how stupid I am. They're looking at you! I forgot that all these people would recognise you . . .'

'Just keep walking,' he said quietly, steering her towards a door opposite them. 'Don't slow down, or we'll never get out of here.'

She quickened her pace to keep up with him. The terminal was not crowded, but a soft murmur began to grow as they hurried through it, until Megan was certain every person in the place was whispering Cam's name. She concentrated on the door ahead, but it was impossible not to see the reactions on the faces they passed. Some people merely looked surprised, pleased to see Cameron Porter so unexpectedly. Some few gaped open-mouthed, until the vacant stare on their faces was replaced by a determined glint and set jaw. Those were the ones who sent a tingle of fear up Megan's spine, because they began to move towards Cam, ignoring everything in their paths as they closed the gap between their victim and themselves.

'Cam?' she whispered uncertainly, glancing up at him. His face was tense, the muscles bunched and tightened in his jaw, and his eyes were unreadable, hidden behind dark sunglasses, but he gripped her waist reassuringly.

'Almost there, love,' he murmured. 'This was foolish of me . . . I should have called ahead, made special security arrangements. Okay,' he said triumphantly, as they reached the doorway. 'We made it.'

He knocked once and the door opened almost

immediately. A uniformed attendant looked at him inquiringly, and then smiled as she recognised Cam.

'*Adelante, por favor, Señor Porter*,' she said, and the door hissed closed behind them.

They were in a small, handsomely furnished room, safe from the noise and curious stares of the people milling outside. Megan leaned against the closed door as relief flooded through her.

'Lord,' she whispered, shaking her head. 'Is it always like that?'

Cam grinned mirthlessly and pushed damp tendrils of hair off her brow. 'No, love, sometimes it's much worse. I've had my shirt ripped off, my face scratched . . . I got a black eye, once, come to think of it, when some woman tried to wrap her arms around my neck just as I turned my head.' He laughed at the look of horror on Megan's face and kissed her lightly on the forehead. 'Don't look like that, Megan. Most people mean well; it's just that some get a bit carried away and forget you're human. At least the press wasn't here, sticking cameras and microphones and lights into our faces.'

She shuddered at the thought of how much worse that would have been. 'I never realised . . . I feel as if we've just run the gauntlet,' she said.

He took her hand and led her to a chair. 'Sit down and relax, Megan. We'll have to run it again in a few minutes, although this time it will be easier. I'll have the attendant arrange for a more private exit and a car outside.' Cam glanced around the empty lounge and frowned. 'Harry—my manager—was supposed to have been here by now. Let me find out if he's got here yet.'

Megan sat back and watched as Cam walked to the far end of the room and spoke with the woman who'd opened the door for them. Another attendant offered her a cup of coffee, which she accepted gratefully. She glanced at Cam again. Was this what it was like to be on the receiving end of public attention and gossip, she wondered? She'd never run after an actor for a story —her subjects, until now, had always been officials or con men—but she'd always thought of them, if she thought of them at all, as being fair game for the media.

'Publicity puts the caviar on their biscuits,' Marian had joked once when an actress had castigated the press for violating the privacy of her honeymoon retreat. 'They complain about it, but they love it.'

It had sounded reasonable then. Now, the memory of the encounter in the terminal still fresh in her mind, she wasn't quite so certain. Cam had suggested that this time, it had been easy. Well, he was used to this sort of thing. Perhaps hers was simply the over-reaction of a novice.

'Megan?' She looked up and smiled at him. 'Harry isn't coming; he phoned about an hour ago. Seems his wife had one of her migraines, and he didn't want to leave her. At any rate, I'll see him for a drink later.' He took her hand in his and helped her to her feet. 'There's a limousine waiting for us just outside, and these people have been very kind. They've assured me that our departure will hardly cause a stir. Shall we leave?'

She nodded and clutched his hand tightly as they walked towards the door. He was right: walking through the terminal and out to the waiting car was quick and simple, but only because a phalanx of security guards served as escort. She felt imprisoned and helpless, not in control of her own fate, and she heaved a deep sigh of relief only when the door of the grey Cadillac had slammed shut behind them. Cam seemed to sense her discomfort.

'It'll be all right once we reach the hotel,' he promised,

as she nestled into the warm security of his encircling arm. 'You'll see.'

And it was. Las Brisas was enormous, a sprawling block of pink set against the cliffs and beach. They were greeted with warmth by the manager and immediately hustled into a pink and white jeep for the short trip to their suite, which he referred to as their *casita*. Flowering hedges surrounded the *casita*, shielding them from prying eyes, and there was, as Cam had promised, a private swimming pool just outside the door, with deep pink flowers floating on its tranquil surface.

'Oh, how lovely,' Megan whispered, as she stood next to the pool and gazed out at Acapulco Bay. 'It's paradise, Cam, paradise.'

He smiled and laid his arm lightly across her shoulders. 'I knew you'd like it here, Megan.'

She put her arm around his waist and laid her head on his chest. 'How could anybody not like it?' she said softly. 'Thank you for bringing me.'

He turned her towards him and kissed her. 'Just hold on to that thought,' he murmured teasingly, his breath warm against her ear. 'You can thank me properly later.' He grinned as she blushed. 'Just to keep your strength up, I'm going to feed you first. Shall we order something from room service, or would you like to go down to the beach and try the buffet?'

'Lunch on the beach? That sounds . . .' She broke off and shook her head. 'Room service, please,' she said quickly, remembering how it had been at the airport.

Cam kissed her gently and then patted her lightly on the bottom. 'I know you'd prefer the beach,' he said. 'Go and change into that swimsuit we bought in Durango. And don't worry about me, Megan. This crowd will let us alone.'

'Are you sure?' she asked doubtfully.

'I'm sure. Now, scoot. Or shall I help you get into that suit?'

She laughed, snatched up one of the brightly wrapped boxes, and hurried into the bedroom.

He had been right about being left alone, she thought a while later. At least, he'd almost been right. Clearly, Las Brisas was used to dealing with celebrities. The staff were pleasant, concerned but not fawning in their attentiveness. The guests buzzed among themselves for a while, but, with the exception of a blushing young couple and a middle-aged woman who seemed annoyed when Cam pleasantly but firmly refused to autograph the back of her bathing suit, people kept a discreet distance. The ambience of La Concha Beach was magnificent. Megan had expected a lavish luncheon buffet spread on tables on the sand, with the Bay serving as background, but she had not anticipated the two salt-water pools hewn from the face of the cliff and connected to the open sea, nor the seemingly endless assortment of delicacies so artistically displayed on the buffet.

She sighed and shook her head when Cam asked if she wanted more lobster. 'Not one bite more,' she groaned. 'This bathing suit barely covers me as it is; if I eat anything else, I'm afraid I'll never fit into it again.'

He smiled at her and ran his fingers through her hair. 'Don't let that stop you. We can always toss out the suit and use our private pool.'

Megan coloured as she returned his smile. 'I'm not convinced it's as private as all that, Cam.'

'It will be at night,' he assured her in a husky whisper. He bent towards her and touched his forehead to hers. 'Unless you want to give it a try right now.'

Her blush deepened. 'You have to wait at least an

hour after eating before you can go swimming,' she said firmly. 'Didn't you know that?'

'Who's talking about swimming?' he teased.

She began to smile, and then her eyes slid past him. A group of ten or twelve people behind him were staring at them with fascination. Even when her eyes caught theirs, no one turned away. Megan cleared her throat and frowned.

'How can people do that?' she murmured. 'It's as if we were on exhibition or something.'

Cam glanced over his shoulder. 'My fault,' he said tightly. 'I'll have to remember to keep my distance from you while we're in public. If I don't, they'll be all over you, as well as me. As it is, you're bound to find yourself whispered about.' His mouth narrowed. 'Maybe we shouldn't have come here,' he said gruffly. 'I should have known better than to think it would work.'

'I'm sorry, Cam,' she whispered unhappily.

'For what?' he said, almost angrily. 'I wanted to show you Acapulco. And I forgot what it would be like . . . it's been so long since I went anywhere like this.' He laughed bitterly. 'Well, at least when you read about the woman Cam Porter was seen with at Las Brisas, you'll know it was you and not some mysterious *femme fatale*, some woman who poses a threat to our relationship . . . although they'll probably twist your description so much that you'll begin to wonder if I ran off and had some secret assignation while you were in the shower or taking a nap or . . .' He shook his head and forced a smile to his face. 'I'm sorry, Megan. I didn't mean to spoil things for you. I just can't help thinking . . .'

Megan knew he was thinking of his wife, and how this kind of thing had hurt her. Deliberately, she stood up and took his hand.

'We didn't come here just to sit around the pool, did

we?' she asked in a crisp, bright voice. 'You said there were lots of things you wanted to show me, Cam. Well, I'm ready to see them all.' He got to his feet and she smiled at him, completely ignoring the stares of the curious. 'And I don't give a damn if they whisper about me or print a thousand mixed-up stories. I know the truth, and that's all that counts.'

The tension eased from his face as he looked at her, and finally he smiled slowly.

'That was quite a speech,' he said quietly. 'Did you mean it?'

'Every word,' she assured him as they walked hand in hand towards their *casita*. 'We came here to have fun, didn't we? Well, I'm not going to let anyone stop us.'

His hand tightened on hers. 'In that case,' he said quickly, 'let's have some.'

Cam seemed determined to show her every inch of Acapulco. Dressed in shorts and cotton pullovers, they walked through the market-place, admiring the hand-thrown pottery and delicate silverwork on display, haggling over the price of a pair of leather sandals that Cam insisted made her look like a Greek goddess. They strolled along deserted beaches, pausing to sift the white sand for jewel-like shells tossed up by the restless ocean. Cam had bought a huge sombrero, and Megan giggled when he put it on, but the hat, combined with his dark glasses, seemed to protect him from all but the most observant tourists.

At sundown, they stopped for a drink at a café and sat on a terrace facing the ocean, solemnly raising their glasses in a toast to the great crimson sun as it slowly descended into the sapphire water. Megan sighed and bent to massage her tired feet.

'Can't we sit here for a little longer?' she pleaded as Cam stood up.

'Does your ankle hurt?' he asked quickly, and she shook her head.

'No, it's fine. It's just my feet that are protesting . . .'

'Then it's time to find a *colandria*,' he said, holding his hand out to her.

Megan frowned as she got to her feet. 'A what?'

'A *colandria*,' he repeated, smiling at the puzzled look on her face. 'Those are the open carriages we passed before. There's nothing quite like seeing Acapulco the old-fashioned way, in a horse-drawn carriage, Megan. And this is the perfect time; almost everybody spends the next couple of hours in their hotel rooms, resting up for the night ahead.'

He was right, of course. The streets were all but deserted. The bustling daytime crowds had vanished as if by magic, and the evening revellers were still preparing for the long hours of dining and dancing that lay ahead. There was a charm to Acapulco that had been missing earlier, and Megan was enchanted by it.

'Now,' Cam said briskly when at last they got back to Las Brisas, 'go on and get changed for the evening.' He glanced at his watch. 'I promised to meet my manager at the bar for a drink, but I'll be back soon.'

'But what will I wear? Now that I've seen this place, I don't think any of the things I bought this morning will do.'

He smiled and touched her cheek. 'You'd look wonderful no matter what you wore,' he said softly. 'But I think you'll find something you'll like waiting in the bedroom.'

He was gone before she could ask any questions. She hurried into the bedroom, smiling with delight when she saw the dress lying across the bed. It was of pale green silk, the fabric so fine it seemed almost translucent. They had seen the dress earlier in their whirlwind day. Cam had wanted to buy it for her, but she'd insisted it was too expensive. How had he managed to purchase it, she wondered, as she ran her hand across the soft, flowing skirt. And sandals to match . . . She smiled again, remembering how he'd urged her to go to the back of the little shop and browse. He must have arranged it then, she thought, while she was poking through a stack of wool serapes . . .

The jangling of the telephone startled her. She reached across the bed and snatched up the phone.

'Cam?' she said.

'Such familiarity, woman. My name is *Señor* Smith.'

Megan smiled to herself. 'They all say that,' she purred. 'Just refresh my memory, would you? Which *Señor* Smith are you?'

He chuckled softly. 'The one who knows you have a tiny birthmark right next to . . .'

'Ah, that *Señor* Smith,' she giggled. 'How are you, *Señor*?'

'Annoyed, that's how I am. Harry is late—he called me at the bar and said he's just leaving his hotel. I'm going to be tied up for at least another forty-five minutes, Megan. I'm sorry.'

'Don't be silly,' she said quickly. 'I'll need at least that long to fix myself up properly so I can do justice to this gorgeous dress. Thank you, Cam. It's a wonderful gift.'

'You're welcome, love. And you're wrong, you know. I just hope the dress does justice to you. See you soon.'

Megan smiled as she hung up the phone. Even the sound of his voice made her happy, she thought, shaking her head in surprised pleasure. To think that a simple telephone call could leave her this warm, this content . . .

She sprang up from the bed and stared at the phone. She'd almost forgotten the call to be made to Marian.

This was the time to do it—there might not be another chance. But she couldn't make it from this suite, where it would appear on the bill. She could reverse the charges, she thought, reaching for the receiver. No, she sighed, that was no good. Marian would know she was in Acapulco. Cam had said he'd be gone for three quarters of an hour. That was enough time . . .

She snatched up the room keys and hurried out of the door. Where had she seen telephones in the hotel? There were some in the lobby and others near the pools. She was out of breath by the time she reached the first bank of phones she could find. Quickly, hands trembling, she snatched up the receiver, mentally blessing whoever had invented telephone credit cards. She twisted the cord impatiently as she waited for the call to go through, and at last she heard Marian's voice.

'It's Megan,' she whispered hoarsely, glancing over her shoulder. 'Listen, Marian, I'm sorry to bother you at home, but . . .'

'Megan? Where the hell are you? I was beginning to wonder if I'd ever hear from you again.'

'Marian, listen to me,' she said urgently. 'I have to tell you something . . .'

'I should hope so, my dear. What have you been doing down there? You have found our boy, haven't you?'

'Marian, please . . .'

'Megan, I want to know everything. Where is he? Have you got any photos? He hasn't caught you, has he? When are you . . .'

'Marian, I'm quitting my job,' she blurted. 'I'm sorry to run out on you this way, but . . .'

'You're what? Megan, what the hell is going on?'

'Nothing is going on,' she said rapidly. 'I haven't found Cam Porter. For all I know, he lives on Mars. I'm quitting, Marian. I'm not coming back.'

'Are you insane? Megan, listen to me . . .'

'Goodbye, Marian,' Megan whispered. 'I'm sorry.' She hung up the phone and wiped her sweating hand on her skirt.

It was done, she thought, as she ran back to the *casita*. She was free at last. She opened the door to the suite carefully, breathing a sigh of relief when she saw that it was still empty. Hurrying into the bathroom, her heart lighter than it had been in days, she turned on the shower.

She emerged moments later, humming tunelessly. She patted herself dry with an enormous, fluffy towel, waltzing with it as she entered the bedroom. The silk dress fitted perfectly, clinging to her breasts and narrow waist, flaring out softly at her hips, and the sandals seemed to glide on effortlessly.

'Just like Cinderella,' she sang loudly, as she spun in a circle. 'That's who I am—I'm Cinder . . .'

Her improvised song ended abruptly as she danced into the living-room. Cam was sitting on the couch, grinning broadly.

'I didn't know you were back,' she said breathlessly. 'I never would have sung if I'd known . . . I have a terrible voice, but for some crazy reason, I love to sing . . . Why are you looking at me like that?' she demanded. 'Doesn't the dress fit? Is it too tight? Cam, for heaven's sake . . .'

'It's amazing, the things you don't know about some-body until you share a room,' he said innocently. 'For instance, if I'd known about your vocal talent, I'd have told you to sing your heart out that night in the woods. No self-respecting bear would have dared . . .' He ducked his head as she grabbed a pillow from a chair and tossed it at him. 'Can't take a compliment, huh?' he laughed, getting to his feet.

She crossed the room towards him, trying to keep a severe look on her face, but it was impossible. Pausing a few feet from where he stood, she pirouetted gracefully and smiled.

'Stop playing music critic and tell me how I look,' she said, tilting her head to the side. 'Do I look good enough for Acapulco?'

'You look too good to share,' he said softly.

'Tell me more,' she laughed as his arms closed around her. 'I love compliments.'

'Is that all it takes to make you happy?' he teased.

She laughed again, almost giddy with the freedom she felt, now that the call to Marian had been made.

'That's all it takes,' she said lightly.

'I'm delighted to hear it,' he said, gently pushing her from him. 'I like a woman who's easy to please.' He brushed her lips with his and smiled. 'Just give me five minutes to shower and change, and we'll be ready to take on Acapulco.'

She smiled as she watched him walk towards the bedroom. She was ready to take on the world, she thought with a sigh of relief. Her link to *Sophisticate* was a thing of the past. Cam Porter, and the love she felt for him, was the future.

CHAPTER ELEVEN

THE Land Rover bounded lightly from side to side as it approached Las Montanas en Cielo. Megan stirred sleepily and lifted her head from Cam's shoulder. She yawned lazily and stretched.

'Did you get any sleep?' he asked.

She shook her head and ran her fingers through her hair. 'No, not really. You're the one who must be tired.' She leaned towards him and ran her finger lightly across his mouth. 'You look so tense . . . You should have let me drive for a while.'

'I'm fine, Megan. I've just been doing a lot of thinking, that's all.'

'Me, too,' she said. 'I keep thinking about Acapulco. It seems as if it's a million miles from here.'

'Yeah, it does. The time went quickly, didn't it?'

She smiled and leaned her head back against the seat. 'Yes, it did. But I'll never forget how wonderful it was.' She chuckled softly and glanced at him. 'Even what you did at La Perla, Cam. You really had those awful people at the next table convinced that you'd won a trip to Mexico in a Cam Porter look-alike contest. As a matter of fact, I was half-tempted to believe you myself! How could you keep a straight face?'

'They deserved it,' he said lightly. 'I wouldn't have minded if they'd asked for my autograph, but when they drew their chairs up to our table and started to tell us all about their daughter Milly or Molly or whatever her name was, and how great she was in her school play, I knew we'd never get rid of them unless I came up with

165

something fast. It worked, didn't it?'

'Worked?' Megan laughed as she recalled the couple's eyes glazing over with boredom as Cam, in a soft drawl, described his life as an Iowa pig-farmer in tedious detail. 'When we were leaving, I heard her tell him that she couldn't believe that even an Iowa pig-farmer could be that boring. They fell for every word.'

'Why wouldn't they, Megan? I'm an actor, after all.'

She nodded in agreement. 'I know, but I when I think of acting, I picture a set and props and a script . . .'

'I'm an actor,' he repeated, 'not an amateur. I don't need anything but an audience.'

'Oh, I'm convinced of that,' she laughed. 'Those people didn't have three words to say to us after that. If you hadn't got rid of them, we'd have completely missed the cliff divers and they were wonderful.' She turned and smiled at him. 'Everything was wonderful, wasn't it? The whole night was like a dream.'

The trees began to thin as the Land Rover began the final climb towards the ranch. 'And there's reality,' he said, as Las Montañas en Cielo came into view. 'All dreams end.'

She looked at him and frowned. There was a toneless quality to his words that disturbed her. Something was troubling him, she thought, as she looked at the downward curve of his mouth and the furrows between his eyes. Busy with her own thoughts, alternating between happiness as she relived the hours in Acapulco and nervousness as she tried to plan when and how to tell him about herself, she'd welcomed the silence in the car. With a twinge of guilt at her own self-centredness, it occurred to her that she'd paid no attention to how withdrawn he'd become the closer they got to the ranch.

'Cam?' she said quietly, 'is something bothering you?'

He pulled into the clearing in front of the house and

turned off the ignition and the quiet of the warm afternoon settled around them.

'I was going to wait until later,' he said finally. 'I'm not
sure this is the right time to tell you.'

'Tell me what?' she said lightly. 'You make it sound so
mysterious.'

'I wish there were an easier way to do this, Megan. I
didn't think things would get this complicated . . .'

An icy chill whispered on her skin. She took a deep
breath and managed to smile reassuringly. 'It can't be as
terrible as you make it sound.'

He pulled the key from the ignition and stared fixedly
at his hands as he ran his finger along it. 'That all
depends on your viewpoint,' he said.

'I see,' Megan said carefully. She waited for him to say
something to ease the tension building between them,
and then she cleared her throat. 'You make it sound
critical,' she said after seconds had ticked by in silence.'

'It is critical, Megan. It's going to change everything . . .'

The sound of the door to the house swinging open
made them look up to see Maria hurrying towards them.

'*Señor* Porter,' she called, '*Señor* . . . ah, I am so glad
you have arrived.' Her dark eyes skittered to Megan's
face and then back to Cam's. 'Andres wished to see you,
Señor,' she said breathlessly. 'He has need to speak with
you.'

Cam scowled as he got out of the car. 'Maria, I'm
busy. I'll be right in.'

The housekeeper shook her head. 'You must come
now, *Señor*,' she said firmly. 'The foreman says it is
urgent,' she added emphatically, glancing at Megan
again. 'This matter cannot wait.'

Cam shrugged his shoulders and put down his suitcase. 'Where is he, Maria? In the stable?'

'This does not concern the horses, *Señor*,' Maria said. 'Andres awaits you in the library.'

He nodded. 'Why don't you wait for me on the terrace, Megan?' he said, turning towards her. 'I'll be as quick as I can. Now that I've started this, I want to finish it.'

The afternoon sun was high overhead, but a cool wind was blowing. Megan shivered and wrapped her arms around herself as she walked to the low railing and gazed up at the mountain looming omnipotently in the distance. Maria had seemed so agitated, so upset. The housekeeper hadn't even spoken to her. She thought of the over-friendly, slightly tipsy tourist who'd taken their photo the night before as they dined on the patio of a restaurant high on the cliffs over the harbour. Could that picture have reached the papers? If it had, if someone had seen it . . . She shook her head and bit her lip.

'Stop acting like a crazy woman,' she warned herself. No one, except her editor and colleagues at *Sophisticate*, could identify her, and they were thousands of miles away. She glanced at the clock visible inside the house and automatically calculated the time difference. It was almost five o'clock in New York. How strange it was to picture Marian and the others heading out into the crowded streets, while she stood here in the midst of the wilderness, waiting for Cam. Well, whatever was wrong at the ranch, it didn't involve her.

But Cam's strange behaviour did. What had he said, a few minutes ago? He had something to tell her, something critical that would change everything. It had sounded so ominous, so frightening . . .

The terrace door slid open and then slammed shut. Megan gasped and whirled around. Cam leaned against the door, his face half in shadow.

'You startled me,' she said with a nervous laugh. 'What did Andres want, Cam? Maria sounded as if it was the end of the world.'

'Nothing as dramatic as that, Megan. He had a message for me that came in on the radio while I was away.'

She moved towards him until she could see his face. His eyes were leaden and expressionless.

'Was it bad news?' she asked uneasily.

'No, not for me,' he said, walking past her until he reached the end of the terrace. 'I'm afraid I'm going to have to make this rather quick, Megan. The message Andres gave me was from my agent. They've moved up the shooting schedule on my new film. It was scheduled to start the week after next, but there's been a change. They want me on location in London by the end of the week.'

She waited for him to say more, trying to read what would come next in his face, but it was impossible.

'And?' she whispered finally, as if the single word had taken all her strength.

'And now I feel I owe you an apology. If I'd known, I'd have suggested you to fly back to the States direct from Acapulco. Your departure would have been easier for you that way.'

'My departure?' she repeated dully.

A cool, somewhat amused smile touched his lips. 'I guess I'm not doing this too well, am I? The thing is, I've got to leave for London the day after tomorrow. That doesn't give you a hell of a lot of time to pack and get to Durango.' He frowned and shook his head. 'Aren't I making myself clear? I have a lot to do before I leave the ranch, Megan. I'm afraid we'll have to end our little interlude a bit sooner than I'd planned.'

She reached out and grasped the wooden railing,

holding on to it as if it were the only solid thing left in the world.

'Our little . . .' She swallowed with difficulty, as if the word he'd used to describe their time together were lodged in her throat.

'I enjoyed it, of course, and I'd rather hoped it might last another few days . . .' He shrugged his shoulders apologetically.

'Are you saying . . . are you telling me that what we had . . . what we've been to each other was just a . . . a . . .' Her voice broke and she stared at him incredulously. 'I don't believe you,' she said flatly. 'You're lying.'

He sighed and stepped away from the railing. 'Yes, I was afraid you might say that,' he admitted, as he walked across the terrace. 'That's why I decided to introduce reality slowly. When we were in Acapulco I thought, what the hell, I still have a few days left, and we're both adults. Why end something so pleasurable before we have to? But on the trip back, I began to think about some of the things you'd said to me, and it occurred to me that things might have gone a bit too far.' That same cool, amused smile played over his face again. 'I wouldn't want you to think I'd led you on, Megan.'

His words were echoing and re-echoing in her head. The separate sounds and syllables were comprehensible, but they refused to come together in a way that made sense. The Cameron Porter standing before her was a stranger, she thought wildly. He had changed into a man she didn't know before her very eyes. She took a deep breath and jammed her trembling hands into her pockets.

'Let me get this straight,' she said quietly. 'The important thing you wanted to tell me was . . .' She shook her head abruptly and closed her eyes. 'I want to be sure

I understand, Cam. Are you saying this was just a . . . a
fling for you? That this past week was just a meaningless
affair?'

'Oh, it wasn't meaningless, Megan,' he said quickly.
'You've been of immeasurable help. You see, this film
I've been rehearsing for is a tough one. Everything
about the character I play comes from inside—he's not
so much a man of action as he is one of introspect. My
character's a politician trying to make it back after a
crushing defeat. He's been hurt by a bad marriage, a bad
press—and then he meets a woman, quite by accident,'
Cam smiled. 'I'd just about given up figuring out how to
get into the part. I could work up the feelings such a man
would have fairly easily, but I had difficulty getting the
hang of how an affair would change them.'

'And then I came along,' Megan whispered.

'And then you came along,' he agreed pleasantly. 'I
didn't plan it precisely that way,' he added politely. 'But
you are an attractive woman, Megan and the setting is so
romantic . . .' He shrugged his shoulders and smiled.
'I'm afraid I always have difficulty separating myself
from the character I'm studying. That's what I was going
to tell you when Maria interrupted us. I knew you might
be upset . . .'

'Upset?' she repeated tonelessly.

'But it was a pleasant respite for both of us, wasn't it?'

She felt as if they were encased in amber, two creatures from another era trapped together for infinity
while all around them the world continued its normal
business. She could almost feel the blood moving
sluggishly through her veins.

'I don't believe you, Cam,' she murmured finally,
formulating each word with excruciating precision. 'I
know what I felt—what we both felt. I don't know why
you're saying these things to me . . .' Suddenly, she

raised her eyes to his as a cold fear clutched at her. 'Unless Andres told you something about me . . .'

'What a thought, Megan. What could Andres possibly know that I wouldn't?' He smiled so cruelly and obscenely that she cringed. 'We haven't left much to the imagination these past days and nights, have we?'

She flinched as if he'd struck her. 'Oh, God,' she whispered, blinking back the hot tears that sprang to her eyes. 'I don't believe it,' she repeated softly, more to herself than to him. 'No one could be that good an actor . . .'

'I could,' he said coldly. 'It's what I do best, Megan. It's what I've always done. When I passed myself off as a cowboy, the men I worked with believed me. And after I learned to ski, I travelled the circuit for a few weeks. You'd be shocked at how many ski bums thought I was one of them. The key to it is to live the role. Once I manage that, once I believe I am the character, the people I come in contact with believe it as well.' He stared at her for a second and then turned away. 'I've asked one of my men to drive you to Durango. I didn't think you'd want to stay the night.' He turned back to her and a sensual smile touched his lips. 'Of course, if you do, I'd be more than happy to accommodate you. We could have one last farewell performance . . .'

'Get away from me,' she hissed, the blood draining from her face. 'What kind of animal are you, Cameron Porter?' She took a faltering step towards him, her hands clenched at her sides. 'Two can play at this game, you know. I can use you, the same way you used me. I can tell your adoring public what a cold-blooded bastard you really are.'

He moved forward, his eyes riveted on her face. 'And how would you do that, Megan?' he asked quietly, his voice soft and menacing. 'I'm interested.'

Tell him, a voice whispered deep inside her trembling body. Tell him who you are, what you are. Tell him that you've deceived him every step of the way, that you're as good an actor as he is. Tell him, and salvage at least a shred of pride from this nightmare.

'I'm waiting, Megan,' he murmured. 'Exactly how are you going to play the game?'

She looked at his white, tense face. He was standing only inches from her, his shoulders slightly hunched and his hands on his lips. He was capable of anything, she thought with a shudder. A man like this, who could put a woman through such hell, was unpredictable. It wasn't gossip that had driven his wife to suicide—it was Cam Porter. God only knew what had gone on between them, she thought suddenly, out here in the middle of no-where, with no one to stop him. The glacial hand of fear clutched at her, and she turned away from him without answering.

'Tell anyone whatever you like,' he said in a low, even voice. 'Just be sure not to omit your willing participation in what went on here, Megan. Because, if you do, I'll give an interview that no one will ever forget. I'll detail your every action, your every word. Nothing you did in my bed will be left out. Nothing, Megan. Do you understand me?'

Their eyes met again and held while her heartbeat raced, until Megan bowed her head and turned her back to him.

'There isn't any way to tell you how much I despise you,' she whispered. 'God, how I wish there were!'

She heard the sound of his footsteps as he crossed the tiles behind her.

'Well, I know an exit line when I hear one,' he said. 'The car is waiting for you out front, Megan. You can leave whenever you're ready.'

The glass door slid closed behind him. With an angry swipe of her hand, Megan wiped tears of anger and humiliation from her cheeks. She waited until she was sure he'd left the hall, and then pushed the door open and stepped into the house, eager to collect her things and leave it forever.

She hurried to the guest-room and flung open the door. Her backpack still lay propped against the wall, where she'd left it. Maria had piled the boxes of newly bought clothing on a chair near the bed; with a flick of her hand, she sent them tumbling to the floor. Quickly, she pulled her jeans and shirts from the cupboard and stuffed them into the pack. Voices drifted to her through the open guest-room door, but she paid no attention to them, concentrating instead on packing her clothing with feverish haste. At last, she closed the pack and began to buckle the straps, glancing around the room one last time to make sure she'd stripped it of her possessions. Then she hoisted it on her shoulders and stepped into the hall.

'. . . and it is foolish to bring that one here, *Señor*, when you are leaving so soon.'

It was Maria's voice, coming from the kitchen. Megan hesitated, caught by the distress in the woman's tone.

'Damnit, Maria,' Cam growled, 'I'm not asking your opinion. I've already called San Diego. Chris will be here early tomorrow; I simply want you to have things ready.'

There was an angry rattle of pots and then the house-keeper spoke again. 'I shall make up the room, *Señor*.'

'It isn't necessary, Maria. Chris will be in with me. Is that understood?'

Megan drew back against the wall and closed her eyes. She could feel the colour rising in her face, and a bitter taste in her mouth.

'*Sí*,' the woman said stiffly, '*sí, Señor*. I understand. But it is a mistake. You will need your rest, if you are to leave in a few days. And you will not get it this way.'

Megan shivered with distaste as Cam laughed. 'You're not my mother, Maria. I don't want to rest; I want to be with Chris. I gave up this whole damned week, and I'm going to make up for it before I leave for London.'

'I am not the keeper of your life, *Señor*,' Maria answered bitterly, 'only of your home. If you wish to—how do you say—to continue this kind of existence, that is your business. I can only tell you, as I have for years, that it is not good.'

'I appreciate your concern, Maria. But the life I lead is my own.'

Again, there was the sound of pots slamming against the counter. 'That does not make it proper, *Señor*. I tried to convince you of that long ago, even before your wife's death . . .'

Megan put her fist to her mouth and hurried to the foyer. She felt soiled, dirtied—and if she didn't breathe fresh air soon, she thought, as she wrenched open the door, she would never feel clean again.

CHAPTER TWELVE

MARIAN HARDWICK narrowed her eyes speculatively as she stared at Megan. 'You really are impossible, you know,' she said quietly. 'First I get that absolutely insane telephone call from you, and then you turn up in my office a couple of days later to tell me that the call was a mistake and that you'll have a story on Cameron Porter on my desk by tomorrow. And I'm not supposed to ask any questions?' She sighed and shook her head in a gesture of exasperation. 'If you were in my shoes, Megan, would you go along with that?'

'I would, if it were the only way I could get the story of the year,' Megan said positively. 'I told you, Marian, I not only found the man's hideaway, I lived in it. And no one else can write this piece—I have no notes, no photos . . .'

'I still don't understand that. Do you really think someone went through your things before you left his home?'

Megan shrugged. 'Someone must have. The house-keeper, probably. I told you, she tried to warn me about him, but she's devoted to his welfare.'

'And you're not worried about his threat to divulge whatever it is that went on between you down there?' Marian smiled and lowered her voice. 'What did go on, my dear? Was it scandalous?'

'It was an empty threat,' Megan said quickly, ignoring the other woman's question. 'He'd have to face the press and leave himself open to too many personal questions. Besides, I'm not going to write about our . . . our relationship, such as it was, in any detail. It's enough that I describe his home, his life . . . and the ugly way he plays with people.'

'Well, then, go to it. Oh, one last thing—rough out a map for me, will you? I'll get in touch with a free-lance photographer I know in Mexico City and we'll see if he can get us some photos of Porter's ranch.'

Megan hesitated as she walked towards the door. 'That might take a while,' she said slowly. 'I'll have to think about it; there were so many crossover roads and turns . . .'

'Yes, well, see if you can't come up with something by this evening,' Marian said, with a wave of dismissal.

Megan nodded as she shut the door behind her. Why on earth had she lied? It wasn't difficult to tell someone how to find Las Montanas en Cielo, once you knew where it was. And envisaging Cam's reaction to finding reporters and photographers camped outside his house should have filled her with pleasure. The man was rotten to the core, she reminded herself as she reached her cramped office. He'd used her cruelly—why should she suddenly feel protective of him?

She wrenched open the door to her office. It was jammed, as usual, but she was grateful for the slight release of tension the act afforded her. She was filled with anger, not just for Cam but for herself. What would it take to quiet her aching heart? It was incredible that she should be so foolish yet, try as she would, she couldn't seem to reconcile the Cam Porter she'd fallen in love with with the one who had so harshly dismissed her from his life. It was hard to accept that she'd fallen in love with a character in his next film, not with him. Well, she thought grimly, feeding a piece of paper into her typewriter, there was only one way to join the two Cam Porters together and silence the pathetic, romantic waif still agonising inside herself. She flopped into her chair and began typing her article.

'Megan? Are you busy?' Marian's voice trilled with laughter as she pushed the door half open. 'I just have to tell you something you're going to love. I just spoke with Mary—you know, the girl at the switchboard. He knew who you were, my dear. When he threw you off his ranch . . . Cam knew you were a reporter for *Sophisticate*!'

'What?' Megan's hands fell from the keys. 'What are you talking about?'

'He knew,' the editor repeated impatiently. 'That's why your notes and pictures were stolen, Megan. Mary had no idea what kind of assignment you were on, of course. Well, it seems that Porter called here that day at five o'clock. He seemed puzzled when Mary answered —you know, she said "*Sophisticate* magazine, may I help you?" and then he asked if she knew a Megan Stevens.'

'He what?' Megan gasped.

'Isn't it marvellous? And Mary, bless her innocent soul, said Miss Stevens couldn't be reached, that she was on assignment.' Marian began to giggle. 'It's a miracle all he did was throw you out.'

Megan sat frozen in horror as the door swung shut. He'd called here at five o'clock: with chilling clarity, she remembered standing on the terrace, waiting for him, thinking that the office in New York was closing for the day. When he said all those awful things to her, he'd already spoken to Mary. He'd known all about her! Slowly, the pieces began to knit together. She swung away from her desk and buried her face in her hands. How pained he must have been, how wounded. She bit her lip and closed her eyes. Was that why she couldn't superimpose the one Cam Porter over the other? Was it possible—could it be that he had cared for her, that in the hurt and anger of learning the truth about her he'd struck back using the same weapon of deceit she'd used?

On the way back from Durango, he'd been different. Not cruel or cold as he'd been in those last terrible moments, but introspective and thoughtful. He'd said he had something important to tell her. Had he realised she'd fallen in love with him? The man she'd spent the week with wasn't insensitive; he was a man who would have sensed the depths of her feelings. And he'd said, right from the start, that he didn't want to rush into anything, that he still had scars from his marriage. Suppose what he'd been brooding about, what he wanted to tell her, was simply that he wasn't ready for what she seemed to be offering? That would be in character for the gentle, honest man she'd thought he was. Surely all that kindness and concern might change to mindless fury once he found out she'd deceived him.

She stood and paced to the other side of her tiny, windowless office. Why hadn't he confronted her with the information, she thought angrily. He was as much to blame as she. She leaned her forehead against the cool metal of a tall filing cabinet. Face it, she told herself grimly, you're the one to blame. You're the one who lied and cheated your way into his home; you're the one who was too much a coward to tell him the truth. No wonder he'd turned the tables and taken command of the game she'd begun. He'd played by her rules, and he'd won.

Even his conversation with Maria about—what was her name?—Chris—even that made sense. It had sounded as if he knew her well and liked her. Why wouldn't he want to spend some time with someone like that after what she had done to him?

Megan slammed her fist on the top of her filing-cabinet. She'd loved him more than she'd dreamed she could ever love anyone and she'd lost him through her own cowardice and duplicity. A sob caught in her throat. For the rest of her life, she'd have nothing but bitter-sweet memories of the week they'd spent together—and the painful knowledge of how badly he hated her. It was too late to go back, too late to explain. She could do nothing, nothing . . . Yes, she thought fiercely, there was one thing. She could save him one final hurt, one last indignity. She wiped her eyes with the back of her hand and stalked from her office.

'Miss Hardwick is in conference—you can't go in there. Miss Stevens, please . . .'

Megan brushed past her editor's secretary and pushed open the door.

'Marian, I have to talk to you,' she said in a rush. 'I know you're not going to like this.' She gasped and put her hand to her mouth. There were two men seated opposite the editor. One was a slight, balding man with a sheaf of papers in his lap. The other was Cam Porter.

'Come in, Megan,' Marian said quietly. 'I was just about to send for you. This is Arthur Belson, an attorney.' Her eyebrows arched and she smiled frostily. 'I think you know this other gentleman.'

Cam's face was expressionless. His glance was cold and remote as it swept over her and then dismissed her.

'They've come here to tell us they're going to sue if we print your article. I've assured Mr Belson and Mr Porter that, under the First Amendment, we have every right to publish it.'

Belson leaned forward and cleared his throat. 'You have not, Miss Hardwick. Miss Stevens has intruded upon my client's right to privacy. Under common-law provisions, he is entitled to maintain . . .'

'No two juries ever agreed on what constitutes a right to privacy,' Marian interrupted. 'And a court case will only lead to further public airing of Mr Porter's life. It seems to me . . .'

'It seems to me, Miss Hardwick, that you have no knowledge of recent precedents in this matter. Perhaps your legal staff can . . .'

Megan stepped further into the room. 'I can save us all a lot of time,' she said clearly, keeping her eyes on Marian. 'I came to tell you I'm not going to write the article, Marian. As far as I'm concerned, I have no information on Cameron Porter.'

There was a stunned silence. 'What are you talking about, Megan?' Marian said finally. 'Of course you have information.'

'None that I'll divulge.'

The other woman's eyes narrowed warningly. 'Come on, Megan. What is it you want? If this is some childish way of demanding a bonus . . .'

'I'm not going to write about Cam Porter,' Megan said quietly. 'That's final.'

'You have no choice,' Marian said, half rising from her desk. 'Your notes, your films belong to the magazine.'

Megan smiled. 'There aren't any notes or films, remember?'

'Are you crazy?' Marian hissed. 'We'll sue you, Megan.'

Arthur Belson rose from his chair and looked at Megan appraisingly. 'This is all very interesting,' he said mildly, 'but quite meaningless. Why should my client believe you, Miss Stevens? You entered his home under false pretences, you violated his privacy, and now you'd have us think you're not going to use the information you gained? I'm afraid we're not going to buy it.'

'Neither is *Sophisticate*, Megan,' Marian said ominously. 'Do you think you can sell your article to another magazine? I warn you, Megan, our lawyers . . .'

'Of course, if you'll sign a statement for us, Miss Stevens, one we'd consider legally binding . . .'

'Megan, dammit, answer me. Have you been in touch with Lou Evans from *Newsquotes*? I'll tear him from limb to . . .'

'Stop it.' Cam's forceful voice silenced them all as he rose from his chair. 'This isn't getting us anywhere,' he said as he turned and faced Megan. 'No one has asked the obvious question.' His eyes locked with hers as he moved towards her. 'Why aren't you going to write the article?'

She wetted her lips and took a breath. 'I . . . I don't think it's right,' she said softly. 'You're entitled to your privacy.'

He smiled coldly. 'How noble. You lied and schemed to get into my home.'

'Cam . . .'

'To get into my home,' he repeated, his voice rising. 'And now you don't think it's right? Come on, Megan, you can do better than that.'

'It's the truth,' she murmured, tears welling in her eyes. 'Please, Cam, you must believe me. I'm so ashamed . . .'

'How much did *Newsquotes* offer?' Marian demanded. 'They can't buy your story, you know. You've got a contract.'

'Perhaps you expect Mr Porter to offer you some sort of settlement, Miss Stevens,' Belson said. 'You must know that's blackmail.'

Tears began to course down Megan's cheeks. 'Why won't you believe me? I don't want anything from anyone.'

'Give me one good reason to believe you, Miss Stevens.'

'Yes,' Marian snapped. 'I'd like to hear it.'

'They may have planned this between them,' Belson said to Cam. 'It won't change our lawsuit.'

'Stop!' Megan cried. There was a silence so complete that she could hear the ring of the telephone in the outer office and the faint, electric hum of the clock on the wall. She was dimly aware of Marian's angry stare and Belson's bemused expression, but her eyes were riveted on Cam.

'I won't do anything to hurt you,' she whispered finally. 'I know you hate me, and I don't blame you. But you must believe me—until you said all those awful things to me, I never intended to write that story.' Her words began to tumble together like grains of sand in the ocean, unpolished and unplanned. 'Ever since that night the foal was born, I knew I couldn't go through with it. And I wanted to tell you, oh God, how I wanted to. I was afraid, Cam.' She lifted her hands imploringly towards him and then dropped them to her sides. 'I was afraid you'd look at me, just the way you are right now.' Her voice trembled and broke, and she took a deep breath. 'I love you, Cam,' she whispered.

She turned and ran blindly from the room, trying to escape the sound of Marian's cry and the look on Cam's face, ignoring the footsteps pounding behind her, wishing she could put a million miles between herself and this place. For once, the door to her office opened at a touch. She slammed it shut behind her and stood, trembling, against the far wall.

'Megan . . . Megan! Open this door.'

It was Cam. She cringed and put her hands over her ears. Hadn't her public admission been humiliation enough? How much more could he demand as penance?

'Megan . . . Dammit, open this door or I'll break it down.'

She closed her eyes as he rattled the knob. The door was jammed again, and it was just as well. She couldn't face him.

Her eyes flew open in astonishment at the sound of splintering wood. The door groaned and fell half way into the tiny room, hanging drunkenly from one hinge. Cam stood in the doorway, filling it, blocking her escape. Megan had a glimpse of startled faces in the hall before he turned and jammed the door closed.

'I told you to open the damned door,' he growled, crossing the small room in two strides. 'Why in hell didn't you listen?'

'Cam, don't . . .' She backed against the wall, her shoulders pressed tightly against its unyielding surface. 'Please, don't . . .'

She shut her eyes as he loomed over her, telling herself she deserved whatever was coming next, waiting for his angry words or the feel of his hand against her cheek.

'Damn you, Megan,' he said, 'I ought to turn you across my knee.'

'I don't blame you for wanting your pound of flesh,' she said desperately. 'But I can't do anything except apologise. I know it isn't enough.'

'Look at me,' he commanded.

She thought of the shattered door and slowly raised her eyes to his, prepared for the worst.

'Repeat what you said in Hardwick's office.' She shook her head, her cheeks blazing with humiliation.

He reached out and grasped her shoulders so hard that she winced. 'Say it,' he demanded.

Megan took a shuddering breath and squared her shoulders. 'I love you,' she said finally, the words a defeated whisper. 'Now are you satisfied?'

Time hung suspended while she waited for his answer.

His fingers bit into her flesh again and then loosened.

'Yes,' he said at last, 'I'm satisfied.'

Her head drooped forward and she sighed. 'Then please leave now. I beg you, Cam, please.'

With a strength and suddenness that made her gasp, his arms closed around her.

'I'll never leave you, Megan,' he said fiercely. 'I love you. I've loved you from the beginning.'

The beat of her heart was like the flutter of fragile wings. 'How can you?' she whispered. 'You don't mean it . . .'

'I never meant anything more. That's why I wanted to hurt you the other day. I was so filled with love for you, and then I found out who you were.' His arms tightened around her and she felt him shudder. 'Andres had tried to call me in Acapulco, to tell me I had to leave for London sooner than planned. My friend in the village asked him if you wanted to place your call to New York again; he joked about how little you'd known about using the radio. Andres was suspicious, and he asked for the number you'd called. I thought maybe there was some man back there you'd been afraid to tell me about, so I tried the number myself.' His voice was muffled as he pressed his lips into her hair. 'When I realised I'd reached *Sophisticate*, when the operator said you were a reporter, I thought you'd betrayed me. It was the worst moment of my life.'

Megan stirred in his arms and looked up at him. 'Cam, I wanted to tell you so many times. I hated myself for deceiving you. But once I knew I loved you, I was terrified that you'd never forgive me for lying to you. And I knew how you hated people like me because of what happened to your wife.'

'My wife was ill, Megan,' he said slowly. 'She was sick long before the gossip columnists made me a target, but I guess it was easier for me to blame them than to admit to myself that she wasn't going to get better. I'll always hate gossip and I still wouldn't want anybody intruding on Las Montanas en Cielo, but I guess it's natural for people to be curious about an actor's off-screen life. You were right about that.'

'Cam, when we got back from Acapulco, you said there was something you had to tell me, something that might change everything. If it was that you weren't ready to make a commitment to me, I understand.'

He smiled and tilted her face up to his. 'I thought I just made one,' he said.

'I mean a permanent one,' she said quickly. 'I know you weren't ready for anything like this.'

'Give me an hour or two and I'll convince you that I'm ready,' he murmured.

She blushed and took a deep breath. 'But what about Chris?'

His smile wavered and he ran his finger across her mouth. 'Chris is what I wanted to talk to you about, Megan. I had to tell you about that part of my life.'

Megan swallowed and forced herself to smile. 'She must mean a great deal to you.'

'He always will, love,' he said softly.

'What?' Megan's eyes widened with incomprehension. 'Did you say "he"?'

'That's right.' He drew back and his eyes bored into hers. 'Chris is my son, Megan. He's just had his fifth birthday.'

'Your son!'

'I was afraid to tell you about him, Megan. When you talked about your ex-husband and how you'd wanted a child, I thought you'd be happy to take on a ready-made family. But when you said you didn't need anyone else, that there wasn't room for anyone but me in your life . . .'

She shook her head and placed her hand across his mouth. 'Don't say any more,' she whispered. 'I can't believe how badly we've misled each other. I only wanted you to know that I wasn't like your wife, Cam. You'd told me she hated the isolation of the ranch, and I wanted you to know that I'd be happy there, without other people around. But a child? A son?' Her smile faltered and she lowered her lashes. 'Having your child to love would be wonderful, just so long as you understand I might not be able to give you other children . . .'

'Are you proposing to me, woman?' he demanded.

Megan blushed and buried her face against his chest. 'Is that what I'm doing?' she whispered.

'I hope so,' he murmured softly, 'because I'd hate to have to disappoint Maria.'

'Maria? What has she to do with it?'

'Maria thinks it's time Chris and I led a normal life. You see, when Sally became pregnant, she became fixated on the idea that she was going to lose the baby. She refused to leave the ranch, so her psychiatrist arranged to have a Mexican doctor visit her several times; he was supposed to stay with us the week the baby was due.' Cam shook his head and smiled ruefully. 'But Chris didn't co-operate. He was born two weeks early, with no one but Maria and me to help. After the baby came, Sally grew even more unstable. She convinced herself that something terrible would happen to Chris if anybody found out about him. Maria and my vaqueros knew how sick my wife was and they wanted to protect her; they're good, loyal people and just superstitious enough to half-believe Sally's premonition, and so they kept the secret.' Cam sighed and his arms tightened around Megan. 'I know it sounds crazy, but after she died, when I convinced myself the media were to blame, I thought, what the hell, maybe, in her own sick way, Sally had been right. I decided to keep things the way they were. Maybe the only way to keep my son safe was to keep the spotlight off him.'

'And it got out of hand,' Megan said softly.

Cam nodded. 'Exactly. At first, when he was an infant, it was okay if the ranch was his whole world. But as he got older, I realised I didn't want to raise him in a vacuum. He's been with my sister the past two weeks, getting used to the real world, while I was supposed to be looking around for a good boarding-school.'

'He's too young, Cam,' Megan said quickly. 'Couldn't he be with us?'

'You'll be his mother, darling,' he said, brushing her lips with his. 'The decision is yours.'

'His mother,' Megan sighed happily. 'But will he like me? Will he want me?'

'He'll adore you, just as I do. He's a chip off the old block, love. He's got the same tastes as his old man.'

There was a discreet tapping at the door. 'Megan? Uh, are you all right in there?'

'God, I almost forgot. It's Marian. What will we tell her?' Megan whispered.

Cam grinned and hugged her to his side. 'Let me do the talking,' he said firmly, as he opened the door. They stepped out into a hall packed with a throng of curious staff members.

'Arthur, Miss Hardwick, Megan and I have an announcement to make. We've settled our dispute amicably.' He glanced down at Megan and smiled. 'We've agreed to grant *Sophisticate* exclusive photos of our wedding.'

'Wedding?' The word ran through the crowd like a ricocheting shot.

'Our wedding,' Cam continued, while Megan blushed happily, 'which will take place this evening.'

'This evening?' Megan repeated incredulously.

Cam bent and kissed her. 'The mayor is a personal friend,' he whispered. 'Sometimes, being famous isn't so bad.'

People stepped aside as they began to move through the corridor. As they reached the door to the reception area, Marian clutched Megan's arm.

'We're thrilled to get this exclusive, my dear,' she said breathlessly. 'But when will you be back? We were going to give you your own column, with a byline.'

Megan's face glowed with pride and happiness. 'I have a byline,' she said softly. 'It's Mrs Cameron Porter.'